THE RADAR WAR

The Radar War

Germany's Pioneering Achievement 1904-45

DAVID PRITCHARD

With a foreword by
Professor R.V. Jones
CB, CBE, FRS

A William Kimber book
published by

PATRICK STEPHENS LIMITED

First published in 1989

British Library Cataloguing in Publication Data

Pritchard, David
The radar war : the German achievement, 1904-45.
1. Radar. Development. 1900-1950
I. Title
621.3848′09′04

ISBN 1-85260-246-5

Patrick Stephens Limited is part of the Thorsons Publishing Group, Wellingborough, Northamptonshire, NN8 2RQ, England.

Photoset in North Wales by Derek Doyle & Associates, Mold, Clwyd and Printed in Great Britain by Mackays of Chatham, Kent

1 3 5 7 9 10 8 6 4 2

Contents

To
Marilyn and Gareth

Foreword

by

Professor R. V. Jones CB, CBE, FRS

One of the greatest of all impacts of science on warfare originated from the prediction in 1864 by James Clerk Maxwell of the existence of radio waves and their confirmation by the experiments of Heinrich Hertz in 1886 and 1887. In fact it was a double impact, resulting first in the development of wireless telegraphy and sound broadcasting, and then of radar and radionavigation.

The use by both sides of wireless telegraphy in the First World War led to such encounters as Jutland and to the work of Room 40 at the Admiralty in decrypting the Zimmermann telegram; and, of course, in World War II we saw the brilliant work at Bletchley in decrypting Enigma signals, and also the impressive efforts of the German cryptographers in breaking some of our own signals.

We in Britain are inclined to think that radar originated in Britain in 1935, stimulated by the threat from the Luftwaffe that was to materialize so dramatically in 1940. It may therefore come as a surprise to find not only that the basic idea of detecting objects by reflected radio waves had been conceived before the First World War, but also that it had been experimentally demonstrated as early as 1904 by a German engineer, Christian Hülsmeyer.

In this book David Pritchard gives much the fullest account of Hülsmeyer's work that is available in the English language, and he then goes on to tell how radar was taken up by the German Armed Services in the years leading up to, and during, World War II. What he has to tell has added much to my own knowledge and will be of interest to all who are concerned with the history of radar, not only in its technical detail but also in its at times reluctant acceptance by serving officers.

While, for example radionavigation was scorned as an adventitious aid by some of our own senior officers, it is refreshing to find that some of their opponents in the Luftwaffe similarly scorned airborne radar as a nightfighting aid because it was 'unsportsmanlike' (page 68) to depend upon gadgets rather than their own eyes. This led to the delicious incident of a junior officer being forbidden to use his airborne radar because his nightfighting successes with its aid might lead to his winning an Iron Cross Class I before his seniors who disdained to use it. We also learn of the rivalries between different groups of workers, certainly no less divisive than those we ourselves sometimes experienced.

As the story unfolds, with its many manifestations of German competence in the radio field, we in Britain can be increasingly thankful that the intensity of the Luftwaffe threat in the years leading up to 1939 brought our serving officers and scientists together at all levels into a close working relationship: it was this, more than any other factor, which resulted in our lead in the operational use of radar even though in some respects the German equipment was technically better.

Happily, British and German scientists, engineers and serving officers have now been on warm terms of cooperation for forty years, partly in face of a common threat but also from a basis of mutual respect for the other side's achievements.

David Pritchard has enhanced that basis by writing this book.

R. V. Jones.

Introduction

This book is the result of what began as curiosity, turned into an absorbing interest and finally became the subject of serious research. In company with many others after the Second World War, I believed radar was a British discovery and had no idea that Germany had developed it earlier, and even after learning this elementary fact I could not have known that it would eventually lead to many years of correspondence and interviews with German scientists, technologists, designers and historians, all of whom were to give me great assistance and in many cases lasting friendship.

Following an initial (and hopeful) period of research I struck a bad patch. I am told all writers know this feeling of despair. And for a while I was floundering in the dark until I hit on the bright idea of writing to Professor R.V. Jones, Emeritus Professor of Natural Philosophy at the University of Aberdeen who, as Assistant Director of Scientific Intelligence during the war,[1] proved the existence of German radar when many Service chiefs and scientists were sceptical about it. I owe a debt of gratitude to Professor Jones for much kind help and advice, and also for putting me in touch with certain sources in Germany who, up to then, had remained somewhat elusive. I am also grateful for his kind permission, and that of his publishers, to publish extracts from his excellent *Most Secret War* (Hamish Hamilton).

My thanks must also go to Bruce Neale, former Chief Engineer of Marconi Radar, now Technical Consultant and Historian, whose knowledge of British radar is second to none

[1] Also Director of Scientific Intelligence, Ministry of Defence, 1952-1953

9

and who very kindly gave me advice on many aspects of the British programme.

The *Würzburg A* radar discovered in February 1942 near Le Havre and subsequently captured in the daring Bruneval Raid, was dismantled under gunfire by Flight Sergeant C.W.H. Cox MM, to whom I am grateful for his recollections of the raid and his opinion of the technical excellence of the equipment.

The *Würzburg* series of radars, together with the *Darmstadt, Mainz* and *Mannheim* equipments, followed later by the famous *Lichtenstein* airborne radars, were the results of research carried out by the late Professor Dr Wilhelm T. Runge, for many years Head of Development at Telefunken, and with whom I was privileged to correspond for some time. I was gratified to receive a copy of his unpublished memoirs *Ich und Telefunken* in which he outlines the original researches into Telefunken's radar systems, and also throws light on the reasons for the poor relations between himself and Dr Rudolf Kühnhold – a matter of some significance to the German radar programme at that time.

Telefunken themselves, now AEG, have my thanks for opening many doors hitherto closed, and in particular I am grateful to Dr Colin Hamilton of the Early-Warning (Airborne) Department, and Mr G. Wiles of the Publicity Department for their very able assistance.

I am also indebted to many retired members of German industry who played important roles in the design and production of radar systems both before and during the war. I am particularly grateful to Dr Herbert Kümmritz, former Telefunken engineer and Luftwaffe officer, for much useful correspondence and a number of interviews at his home in Ulm, all of which resulted in a clearer picture of some of the difficulties encountered by the Luftwaffe in relation to airborne radar, and a deal of information about the personnel involved in the programme. My thanks also go to Professor Hermann Diehl for copies of his 1942 patent for 'A System for the Guidance of Aircraft' and further details of his pioneering work with the *Freya* radars, and to Dr B. Röde, indefatigable collector of items of radar interest, whose knowledge of German systems is equalled only by an astonishing collection of artefacts. I still retain a vivid picture of the postman staggering to my door with a parcel of prodigious dimensions containing a wealth of military manuals on the operation, servicing and maintenance of the *Freya* series.

In my pursuit of personalities, that of Dr Rudolf Kühnhold,

whose pioneering work from 1929 onwards led to the development of the *Seetakt* and *Freya* series of radars, was probably the most elusive, but I managed to track him down in Kiel, where he began his researches for the German Navy, and where he has since lived, although now laid low by poor health in his 84th year. To him and his son-in-law Dr Claus Kinder I am grateful for a deal of information about those early days and the subsequent founding of the Gema Company.

I am also indebted to Dr Gotthard Müller of Lorenz (now known as SEL) for his kind help, and for permission to use his comprehensive *Funkmessgeräte-Entwicklung bei der Co. Lorenz AG 1939-1945*, a work all the more remarkable for the fact that it was written after his release from ten years of prison camps and forced marches as a prisoner of the Russians. My thanks also go to Dr H. Bosse for much useful information from his seminar notes and other valuable documents.

I am also grateful to David Irving for his kind permission to quote from his outstanding *The Rise and Fall of the Luftwaffe* (Weidenfeld & Nicolson, 1973).

My interest in the work of Christian Hülsmeyer, now acknowledged throughout Germany and most of the western world as the inventor of the world's first practical radar system, received its greatest stimulus after reading contemporary reports, but it was not until I began correspondence with his daughter Frau Annelise Hecker-Hülsmeyer and checked the documents she sent me with the best informed sources, that the stimulus took on the proportions of revelation. To her I owe a great debt for copies of the original patents and documents relating to her father's early work, many of which, to the best of my belief, have never been published, or at best received only scanty treatment, and I am equally grateful for her personal recollections of Hülsmeyer's life and struggles. In this connection I must also thank Professor Weidenhaupt of the Stadtarchiv Düsseldorf for his kind help and for supplying me with details from the New German Biography (1972), and Mjnheer P. van Wijngaarden of the Stadtarchivdienst Rotterdam for his sterling work in tracing the copies of Hülsmeyer's letters to Director Wierdsma of the Holland-Amerika Line, and for sending me the Official Report of the Technical Nautical Meeting at Rotterdam in which Hülsmeyer's successful demonstration is recognised, together with the photograph of the tender *Columbus* which carried his equipment. My thanks must also go to the proprietors of the *Kölnische Zeitung* and *Rhein-Post* for their reports and features on the 1904 demonstrations.

Above all I owe special thanks to Fritz Trenkle, Germany's leading authority and historian on radar and radionavigation systems, whose published works extend over many years, and without whose generous help on points of detail this book would never have been written. I am particularly grateful to him for permission to use photographs from his personal library of some 5,000 pictures, possibly the world's most comprehensive private collection of German systems. For the gift of friendship I owe a greater debt which I prefer to leave unpaid.

Whilst the history and development of German radar still holds a fascination for many persons, its discovery by the British and their subsequent countermeasures are still worth recalling today, not only as a record of determination and bravery, for these were never lacking on both sides, but in many instances as a lesson on the essential requirements of sound Intelligence work, lessons which, if the modern tendency of the wagging tongue is any criterion, have been sadly forgotten. Thousands played major parts in this field during the war, and of those still alive today many prefer to keep quiet about it. Their work is, I hope, reflected in the names of those who have no objection to appearing in these pages.

Finally, though this book must necessarily deal with technical matters, I have tried to keep these to a minimum by assuming a certain degree of technical knowledge among its readers in keeping with our technological age. The steering of a safe channel between the Charybdis of blinding with science and the Scylla of insulting the reader's intelligence is always a Herculean task, and if I have erred either way I can only take comfort from the words of John Locke: 'All men are liable to error, and most men are, in many points, by passion or interest, under temptation to it.'

David Pritchard
1989

CHAPTER ONE

Christian Hülsmeyer, the Father of Radar

Radar may be defined as the art of detecting by means of radio echoes the presence of objects, determining their direction and range, recognising their character and employing the data thus obtained in the performance of military, naval or other operations.

Principles of Radar,
Massachusetts Institute of Technology Radar School

The principle of the reflecting qualities of radio waves upon which radar technology is founded was discovered in 1886-87 by Professor Heinrich Rudolf Hertz (1857-1894) at the Karlsruhe Polytechnic. His experiments were based on Maxwell's theory of electricity and magnetism for which experimental verification was lacking in Maxwell's time. Hertz's experiments demonstrated that ordinary light consists of electromagnetic waves, and the equipment he constructed for this purpose was what we would now call a spark transmitter oscillating (unbeknown to Hertz) on a frequency of about 50 MegaHertz (MHz).

Having proved that these electric waves existed, he followed it up by showing that they could be reflected, refracted, diffracted and polarised in the same way as light can. The velocity of propagation was measured and found to be the same as light and radiant heat. Hertz himself could find no practical uses for his discoveries and it was left to other researchers, notably Sir William Crookes, Sir Oliver Lodge, Marconi *et al*, to employ his findings for the development of wireless telegraphy. But his experiments with metal sheets to reflect these waves may readily be seen as the foundation for radar.

It should therefore be no surprise to learn that the world's first practical radar system was successfully demonstrated a few years later in 1904, and the remarkable history of the discoverer of this system is worth recounting.

Christian Hülsmeyer was the youngest of five children born to Johann Heinrich Ernst Hülsmeyer and his wife Elizabeth Wilhemine (née Brenning) at Eydelstedt, Germany, and made his appearance on Christmas Day 1881. From 1887 to 1895 he attended the primary school in Eydelstedt where his teacher, Rudolf Knüppling, was impressed by his enquiring mind. On returning home one foggy evening the boy witnessed a scene that was to haunt him for a long time. His mother was trying to comfort a weeping woman whose son had been drowned when his vessel collided with another on the fogbound Weser. Horrified at the picture his impressionable mind conjured up, he crept up to his bedroom and sought solace among some old books he had found in the attic. One of his favourites was a life history of Benjamin Franklin and his experiments with electricity.

Later, as the memory of the event lost some of its hurt, he would wander round his father's farm in the evenings and wonder how the bats avoided the trees as they swirled round the farmyard before settling in the barns. He put the question to his grandmother, a woman wise in the ways of nature, who told him, 'They have special noses to help them find their way in the dark.'

The bat is still a feature in the Hülsmeyer coat-of-arms.

From 1895 to 1896 Hülsmeyer received special attention from headmaster Erich Bartels at the Elementary School in Donstorf where, besides French and English, his aptitude for physics was soon spotted. Bartels introduced him to Hertz's work and encouraged him to take the Entrance Examination for the Teachers' Training College in Bremen. After passing the examination Hülsmeyer studied at the College between 1896 and 1900.

The Bremen College boasted a fine new physics laboratory, much of which was devoted to research into the Hertzian Waves, and the Physics Master, Richard Klimpert, gave Hülsmeyer extra tuition and encouraged him to carry out experiments in this new field, allowing him the use of the laboratory after normal college hours. His daughter Annelise recalls a story from this period:

A large oven, something like a kitchen range, occupied one end of the laboratory and my father used its metal surface for his reflection experiments, during which the whole room would be filled with crackles and discharge of sparks from his apparatus. By this means he proved to his own satisfaction that Hertzian Waves could be easily reflected from distant metallic objects.

Encouraged by his results Hülsmeyer devoted much time to the design and construction of more powerful transmitters to increase the range. Impressed, Klimpert took him aside and said, 'Don't waste your time going in for teaching. They need people like you in industry.'

Much against his parents' wishes Hülsmeyer applied for and obtained a position with Siemens and Schuckert in Bremen where he supervised installations and carried out the electrical outfitting of battlecruisers. His daughter continues the story:

> In April 1902 my father left the Siemens Company and made his way to Düsseldorf with only two marks in his pocket. There his brother had a thriving textile business and financed Christian in the setting up of an electrical firm that enabled him to carry out further research into reflection techniques, and to build a transmitter and receiver for the purposes he had in mind. But this needed more money than was available. In the end he placed an advertisement in the local paper for a financier to back him in an 'epoch–making discovery'. A Cologne leather merchant saw it and showed interest.

The leather merchant, Heinrich Mannheim, was a leading figure in Cologne business circles and immediately put up the money for a joint venture. Business premises were obtained and the world's first, albeit primitive, radar was put on the market under the name of the *Telemobiloscope*. The Telemobiloscope Company, Hülsmeyer and Mannheim, confidently awaited orders, but none came. Clearly, an advertising stunt was needed.

On the morning of 10 May 1904 two shadowy figures approached the Rhine bridge at Cologne. Both carried wooden boxes[1] and took up positions on a platform under the middle of the bridge. A policeman wondered what they were up to, but on recognising the respectable Mannheim shrugged his shoulders and sauntered away. A group of reporters arrived and lounged over the parapet. And as time went by a crowd of onlookers gathered.

[1] Some critics of Hülsmeyer's early experiments remark on the lack of screening accompanying the use of wooden cases. In fact Hülsmeyer lined them with metal foil and later employed sheet metal exclusively.

'What are you up to down there?'

Hülsmeyer grinned. He tapped the wooden boxes.

'This is an apparatus for preventing collisions at sea. The electric waves given out by this transmitter are reflected back to this receiver by a vessel, so that it can be detected at night or in fog.'

'Go on, pull the other one!'

At that moment a Rhine barge hove into view several hundred yards down river.

'Wait and see!' yelled back Hülsmeyer.

He turned a switch and the bystanders heard a faint buzzing. They watched as Hülsmeyer directed the antennas at the barge, whereupon a bell rang in the receiver. The crowd roared.

'Can you do the Indian rope-trick as well?'

Undeterred, Hülsmeyer swung the antennas to the sky and the bell stopped. On re-directing them at the barge it rang again. The onlookers scratched their heads – they could not know they had just witnessed a demonstration of the world's first radar – while the reporters legged it hot-foot to hand in their copy.

German and other continental papers flashed the news round the whole of Europe and Hülsmeyer was promptly invited to demonstrate his equipment to the representatives of shipping companies. The *Kölnischer Zeitung* of 18 May 1904 carried the report:

The Telemobiloscope, an invention of engineer Christian Hülsmeyer, was demonstrated to representatives of Norddeutscher Lloyd and the Argo Shipping Company of Bremen and other invited gentlemen at the Dom Hotel yesterday morning at 11 o'clock. The discovery is based on the principle of wireless telegraphy and is intended to locate ships and other metallic objects at sea. The difference between the already existing employment of wireless telegraphy and this discovery is based on an exclusive and constructional change, in that wireless telegraphy employs a transmitter and receiver on separate ships but with the Telemobiloscope the transmitter and receiver are arranged on one and the same vessel. The electrical waves radiated from the transmitter cannot directly reach the receiver, but must be reflected from metallic objects on the sea, logically ships, and thus return to the receiver. The great advantage which the discovery offers lies above all in the fact that ships which are fitted with this system of transmitter and receiver can locate any other ship that does not carry the apparatus. Indeed, the captain on the bridge can be informed of the approach of another vessel and find its bearing up to a range of 5 kilometres, so that should his lights and fog signals fail to work he still has sufficient time to steer his ship on the correct course and thus prevent severe disasters in good time. Research with smaller apparatus calculated for shorter ranges have been perfectly successful. A company for the manufacture of the discovery has been formed under the title of The Telemobiloscope Company, Hülsmeyer and Mannheim.

Emboldened, Hülsmeyer sought more financial help and approached the German Navy. Admiral von Tirpitz's reply was scathing:

'Not interested. My people have better ideas!'

But reports had reached Director Wierdsma of the Holland-Amerika-Line who invited the inventor to demonstrate his discovery at a Technical Nautical Meeting at Scheveningen, and on Thursday, 9 June 1904, assisted by students of Delft University, Hülsmeyer assembled his equipment in the tender *Columbus* and cruised up and down Rotterdam Harbour detecting vessels at up to 5 kilometres' range with unerring accuracy. The only problem was that as eight technical representatives of foreign shipping companies were with him to witness the demonstration he was obliged to take out a similar number of foreign patents, and this cost more money.

The representatives were however enthusiastic about the demonstration and showered Hülsmeyer with praise, and after a lecture in which he explained that even longer ranges were quite possible he waited for orders.

But none came. Not even a trial order.

The list of those present at the demonstration is impressive. The American Line, Leyland Line, and Dominion Line were represented by Captain Fry (Marine Superintendent) and Mr Neville Evans (Superintendent Engineer). The Atlantic Transport Company was supported by Mr Kirkland and Mr Alger, and the Hamburg-Amerika-Line by Mr Klock (Superintendent Engineer) and Inspector Captain Theile. Ober-Inspector Blanke, Ober-Ingenieur Walter, and Ingenieur Struver attended on behalf of Norddeutscher-Lloyd, and Mr Robert Crichton (Marine Superintendent and Superintendent Engineer) for the Red Star Line. Director Wierdsma, Mr van

Helden (Superintendent Engineer), Mr Boldingh (Marine Superintendent), and Mr Muschart (Assistant Marine Superintendent) were present on behalf of the Holland-Amerika-Line.

The minutes of the meeting contain the following report:

The Telemobiloscope

During the visit of the delegates to the establishment of the Holland-Amerika-Line at Rotterdam, a trial was given on board the tender *Columbus* to the Telemobiloscope, an invention of Christian Hülsmeyer Esq., Engineer at Düsseldorf. This apparatus is based on the principle of wireless telegraphy and is intended to ascertain, when at sea, the direction and also the distance of another vessel. In wireless telegraphy the distributor and the receiver are put apart in different places, in the Telemobiloscope they are placed together on the same spot. The electrical currents of the distributor however cannot be caught by the receiver directly but must strike an object of metal (in this case another vessel) before returning to the receiver.

The opinion of the inventor is that vessels fitted with his apparatus can discover at night or in fog etc., at a distance of up to 3½ miles, other vessels and ascertain the position of these vessels. The trial on board of the *Columbus*, though on a very limited scale and with an unfinished apparatus, proved that the principle of the inventor is correct. Every time when, even at a certain distance, a vessel or drydock (both of course of iron or steel) was passed, the apparatus operated immediately.

The apparatus used in this trial was not yet arranged for the determination of the distance.

The Hülsmeyer story is fairly well known but for several years commentators have dismissed his discovery as virtually worthless. Various reasons have been put forward, such as extraneous reflections from the ship itself affecting the receiver, or the technical knowledge at the time being insufficient to make it a serious contender in the radar story. These are simplistic excuses – often, regrettably, emanating from British sources – and which demonstrate a lack of appreciation of the astonishingly modern concepts in Hülsmeyer's system, concepts worthy of greater study and which will be examined later.

But these ill-considered explanations are often advanced to explain why the system failed to have any impact on the world, and in particular the world of shipping for which it was originally designed.

The true facts are as simple as they are condemning.

In the first place, world shipping in 1904 was going through a bad patch and expenditure on even the bare essentials of safety procedures was viewed with reluctance. The evidence of the Technical Nautical Meeting speaks for itself:

> ...it is the doubtfully pleasant duty of the technical department to spend money in an ever increasing degree. Although this is true at all times, it gets a double significance in bad times, as he is sorry to say, we are having now, and the responsibility rests heavily on the technical official, who has incessantly to answer the question: which item may be postponed without risk and which must be done at once, whilst precisely at that time he is expected to effect every economy. Add to this that as a matter of course the technical officer is more exposed to criticism, for the reason that although he himself would be loath to pass judgement on the passenger or freight business, everyone connected with a steamship line possesses a certain opinion in technical matters and even allows himself to be seduced to inventions.

Second, and more important, the arrival of wireless telegraphy was a hindrance to the acceptance of Hülsmeyer's discovery. By 1904 it had been installed in a number of vessels which were now able to communicate with others at distances far beyond the range of visual signalling. In emergencies the wireless operator could quickly call for help, and this had been possible as early as 1901. Moreover, direction-finding by the use of cross-bearings from shore stations enabled a master to fix his position with a fair degree of accuracy. Ship-owners were therefore reluctant to part with money for a new-fangled system when they were already paying enough for the present one.

But the least known, yet most obvious reason for the lack of success, lay in the all-important point that most ship-owners could not distinguish between wireless telegraphy and the concept of radio-location. The very fact that all reports and documents referred to Hülsmeyer's discovery as based on a form of wireless telegraphy was enough to convince them that it was one and the same thing, however different its use, and shipping lines using wireless telegraphy in its accepted sense were mostly under contract to the Marconi monopoly. The terms of the Marconi Licence were strict and no one in those competitive times would dare risk a suit for breach of contract.

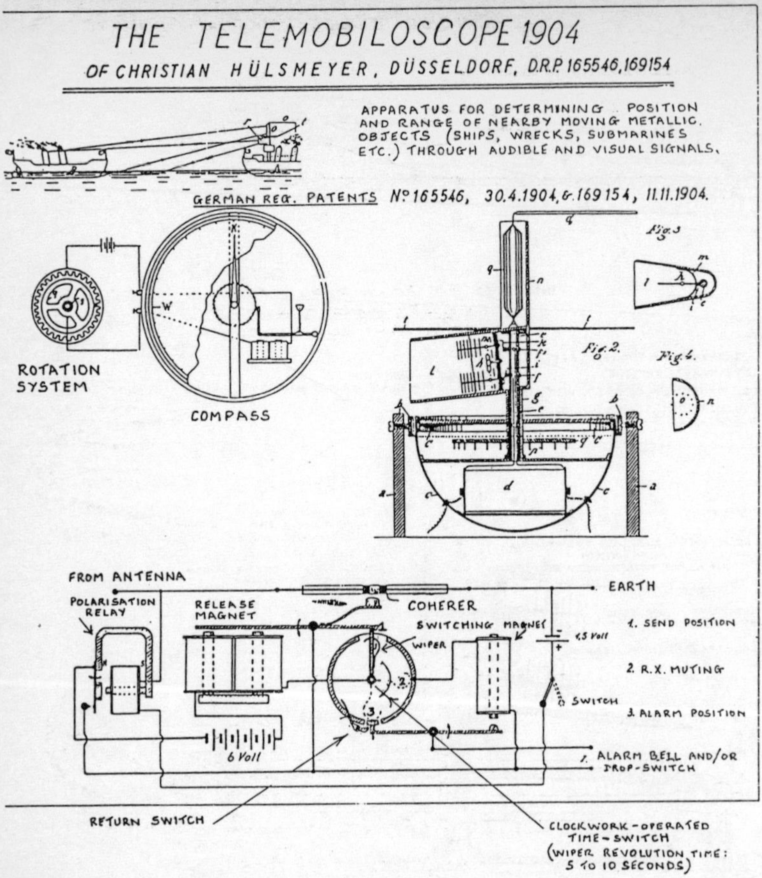

THE TELEMOBILOSCOPE 1904
OF CHRISTIAN HÜLSMEYER, DÜSSELDORF, D.R.P. 165546, 169154

APPARATUS FOR DETERMINING POSITION
AND RANGE OF NEARBY MOVING METALLIC
OBJECTS (SHIPS, WRECKS, SUBMARINES
ETC.) THROUGH AUDIBLE AND VISUAL SIGNALS.

GERMAN REG. PATENTS Nº 165546, 30.4.1904, & 169154, 11.11.1904.

ROTATION
SYSTEM

COMPASS

FROM ANTENNA
POLARISATION RELAY
RELEASE MAGNET
COHERER
SWITCHING MAGNET
WIPER
EARTH
1. SEND POSITION
2. R.X. MUTING
3. ALARM POSITION
SWITCH
6 Volt
4. ALARM BELL AND/OR
DROP-SWITCH
RETURN SWITCH
CLOCKWORK-OPERATED
TIME-SWITCH
(WIPER REVOLUTION TIME:
5 to 10 SECONDS)

Figure 1 Christian Hülsmeyer's 'Telemobiloscope' of 1904.

The world's first radar just refused to sell.

Anxious to save as much of the situation as possible Mannheim embarked on a sales drive, but the major electrical companies of the time showed no interest. Even Telefunken, then known as The Wireless Telegraphy Company, replied on 21 August 1905:

Dear Sir,

Please find enclosed the Patent Specifications you kindly offered us a short time ago for 'A System of Reporting Distant Metallic Objects to an Observer' and the addition to Patent No.32910 VIII/74D by Christian Hülsmeyer of Düsseldorf.

We return these with our best thanks as we have no use for the above discovery.

Yours faithfully,
The Wireless Telegraph Company

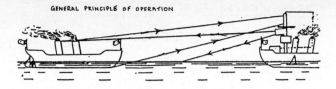

GENERAL PRINCIPLE OF OPERATION

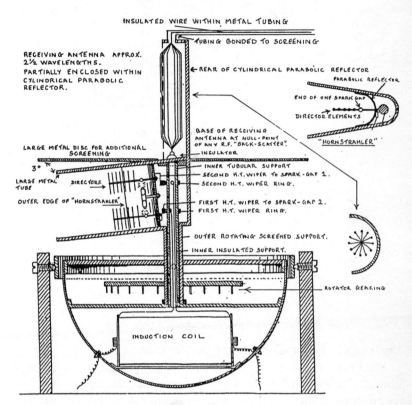

Figure 2 The equipment in more detail.

Annelise Hülsmeyer adds the following:

> Herr Mannheim himself took pains, unfortunately in vain, to obtain orders from industry (Telefunken, Felten, Guillame, etc.) but the answers were unsatisfactory. Clearly no one had given any real thought to it. And in order to eat, my father thrust all the drawings and patents of his first and dearly-loved discovery in a drawer of his desk and turned to other interests.

A study of the Hülsmeyer technique reveals astonishingly modern concepts, many of which were not to see the light of day until another thirty years had elapsed and in some cases

even longer. Even the most cursory examination proves that
the inventor was years ahead of his time. The Patent
Specification Drawings of even his first design show that the
entire structure is completely screened with metal to reduce
stray fields and is mounted on a compass-like box, the gimbals
ensuring a reasonable vertical position in a seaway. Rotation
was provided by a foolproof solenoid and ratchet system, and a
repeater compass on the bridge gave the officer of the watch an
instant bearing when required.

The induction coil for the spark gaps[1] was housed in the
compass box and insulated cables suitably spaced to prevent
arc-over were conducted over an insulated shaft in a metal
column, the power being delivered to the spark gaps by a brush
and ring system. The spark gap itself was a partially
oil-immersed Righi model and its position relative to the other
components within the radiation system is interesting. Situated
at the focal point of a concave reflector the two gaps were
furnished with a double array of what appear to be director
elements, the whole bearing a strong resemblance to a slotted
Yagi-type beam system – an arrangement all the more
remarkable since more than twenty years were to elapse before
Professor Yagi of Japan introduced the beam antenna that
bears his name. The entire antenna array was contained within
a funnel-shaped reflector called a *Hornstrahler*, or 'horn-
beamer' which in turn was enclosed in a larger cylindrical metal
casing. When it is remembered that the operating wavelength
was about 50cm[2] (as determined later by Telefunken
engineers) it is hardly surprising if the structure resembles a
waveguide, a notion not as astonishing as it seems when it is
remembered that only a few years earlier Lord Rayleigh had
announced that radio waves could be passed along a length of
18-inch metal pipe and emerge at increased strength at the
other end.

[1] Although the spark transmitter was the only known method of
transmission in those days, it is unwise to relegate it merely to the position of a
primitive system and nothing more. Such transmitters were capable of
generating large powers, and it is interesting to note that during the Second
World War the Germans made use of the technique for their *Grete II* radar
which delivered *one megawatt*, i.e. one million watts. See page 195.

[2] It is interesting to note that this wavelength, corresponding to about 600
MHz, was used some thirty years later by engineers who had never heard of
Hülsmeyer's work. The employment of centimetric waves for German radar
was a distinguishing feature throughout its history, and in 1934 it was laid
down that engineers should concentrate on 50 cm. See page 39.

The receiving antenna was a cage of wires of some two and a half wavelengths mounted in a vertical cylindrical reflector bonded to the screening of the entire structure with a large circular metal disc between the two arrays to reduce stray fields to a minimum. It is also interesting to note that the position of the receiving antenna is in a null area of any possible rear lobes. And of greater interest is the provision of coaxial cable bonded to the screening of the assembly by which the received echo was delivered to the receiver, the latter being situated at a convenient point in the ship. Examination of the receiving equipment shows a common coherer system utilising the broadly-tuned antenna system, but the outstanding feature is Hülsmeyer's incorporation of his *Zeitsperre*, or 'time-barrier', which was a motor-driven rotating switch synchronised with the rotation mechanism of the whole assembly, which allowed the receiver to ring a bell or to actuate a drop-switch only on the reception of a second signal. A further refinement was the adoption of a command signal of three morse characters which alone actuated the receiver.

The range of the early system was about 5 km. The assembly was designed for mounting on the foremast of a ship at a pre-determined height, range-finding being carried out by raising or lowering the assembly on reception of an echo and employing triangulation or simple trigonometry with use of a pre-prepared scale of figures. Later, Hülsmeyer employed a system of range-finding that made use of radio lenses of a bitumastic-type dialectric in a double concave assembly – and radio lenses together with horn antennas were not to be seen again until the Second World War!

In hindsight it is astonishing that this system failed to interest the maritime world of those days. Some commentators have asserted that this lack of foresight was nothing less than criminal, even hinting that the *Titanic* disaster might have been averted had the vessel been equipped with this discovery – but stable doors had ever been shut on inventions the contemporary world fails to appreciate – and the passing of time often confers on those unrecognised in their own lifetimes a belated recognition even when their original art is overtaken by the advance of technology and science. Only after the end of the Second World War was Hülsmeyer hailed in his own country as the discoverer of the world's first practical radar system, a matter stonily ignored in the United Kingdom.

On reading Churchill's rhetorical question after the war

regarding the *'unknown inventor of radar'*, Hülsmeyer's daughter sent a letter to the great man:

Düsseldorf, April 18 1949

To the Rt Hon Winston S. Churchill,

For several months the German press have carried articles under the title 'Churchill's search for the Inventor of Radar'. In these articles the writers refer to a passage in your Memoirs in which you appreciate the work of the unknown inventor of radar. I must tell you that this unknown inventor is my father, the engineer Christian Hülsmeyer of Düsseldorf who was born in 1881.

Shortly after Marconi's invention of wireless telegraphy my father was granted the German Patent No. 165546 on the 30 April 1904 for his apparatus known as the Telemobiloscope, which was tested in May of that year in Cologne. This demonstration was reported around the world, the *New York Times* of 19 May 1904 reporting:

> *Signal Approach of Ships*
> *German Engineer's Invention*
> *Tested in Cologne*

Berlin May 18

An engineer named Hülsmeyer from Düsseldorf gave a demonstration to the shipping interests at Cologne today of an invention called the Telemobiloscope, by which a steamship captain will be able to detect the presence and direction of any other steamship three miles away. The apparatus consists of …

After this result my father offered his invention to the German Navy in the hope that naval engineers and scientists would give consideration to the system, but the offer was refused. My father then took out patents in all other countries including England where he was granted the following:

Patent No. 13170 dated 10.6.1904 for a 'Hertzian-Wave Projecting and Receiving Apparatus Adapted to Indicate or Give Warning of the Presence of a Metallic Body, such as a Ship or a Train, in the Line of Projection of such Waves.'

Patent No. 25608 dated 24.11.1904 for 'Improvements in Hertzian Wave Projecting and Receiving Apparatus for Locating the Position of Distant Metallic Objects.'

Following the publication in the press of this invention, Director Wierdsma of the Holland-Amerika-Line invited my father to demonstrate his invention at the Technical Nautical Meeting in Rotterdam on 9.6.1904 before technical representatives of eight international shipping lines. The Dutch newspaper *De Telegraaf* on 10.6.1904 informed the world in detail about the demonstration. After this, my father hoped that one of the shipping lines would introduce his apparatus to prevent collisions between ships, but they preferred to use Marconi's wireless telegraphy instead.

The several demonstrations and work on his invention had cost my father nearly 25,000 marks, and as he was unable to bear the costs of maintaining his patents, he allowed them to lapse.

After the technical development of forty years my father's *Telemobiloscope* principle was embodied and completed in the 'Radar' of Sir Robert Watson-Watt. A German invention for the victory of the Allies!

Yours respectfully,
Annelise Hülsmeyer

Not surprisingly perhaps, especially in view of the sentiments in the final paragraph, Churchill sent a terse reply:

Figure 3 Hülsmeyer's patent, dated 30 April 1904 (*Fritz Trenkle*).

28, Hyde Park Gate, London, S.W.7
28 July 1949

Dear Sir,
   I am desired by Mr Churchill to thank you for your letter, which it has given him interest to receive.

Yours truly,
[signed] Private Secretary
Miss Anne-lis Hülsmeyer

which confusion over the sex of the addressee is surely inexcusable. At about this time Hülsmeyer's daughter married the engineer Erich Hecker who, a year later, sent the following letter to Churchill:

Düsseldorf 12 February 1951

To
Lord (sic) Winston S. Churchill
28, Hyde Park Gate, London S.W.7
In our daily paper, the *Rhein-Post* of 9 February 1951, I read that in your country at this time Sir Robert Watson-Watt is to be celebrated and recognised as the discoverer of radar. With full appreciation and acknowledgement of the radar system developed by this outstanding gentleman, I must not fail to draw to your attention once more the Patents already existing in England, numbers 13170 and 25608, of the year 1904, and relating to an equipment known at that time as a Telemobiloscope.
   This had been successfully demonstrated in 1904 at the International Shipping Congress in Rotterdam and is therefore the first radar discovery and the forerunner of today's radar. Records and evidence to support the truth of my statements have already been received by you in 1949 from the daughter of the German discoverer, and I am convinced that as an outstanding statesman you will not permit the abstaining of an impartial and critical examination of these facts.
   I write as the son-in-law of the 70-year-old discoverer with the hope that a possible recognition of these facts on your part will give great pleasure to him, if only in the short evening of his life.

Very respectfully yours,
Your obedient servant,
Erich Hecker

Churchill's answer had at least the merit of being longer:

House of Commons
London, S.W.1
23rd February 1951

Dear Herr Hecker,
Thank you for your letter of the 12th February which Mr Churchill has asked me to answer on his behalf.
I very much regret that it would not be possible for him to intervene in the question of your (sic) invention. You should take this matter up with your legal adviser.

Yours sincerely,
(signature illegible)
Hon. Secretary.

Nothing daunted, Hecker wrote the following month to the British Patent Office:

Düsseldorf, 5 March 1951

To the President of the Patent-Office
of Great Britain, London.
From our daily paper, the *Rhine-Post*, of 9 February 1951 I note that Sir Robert Watson-Watt is to be honoured and acknowledged as the discoverer of radar and has applied for a Patent for his discovery in 1935. With full appreciation and acknowledgement of his merits in the development of this apparatus, which is one of the major discoveries of the last decade, permit me politely to draw your attention back to the year 1904. It will doubtless interest you that already by that time, thirty years before the patent application by Watson-Watt for his discovery, in almost every European country including England an equipment had been patented that worked on the same principle as today's radar and was known by the name of a Telemobiloscope. This was successfully demonstrated before experts at the International Shipping Congress in Rotterdam in 1904. The established facts of this demonstration are evidenced by the Dutch newspaper *De Courant* of 8 July 1950, which in its account also reproduced an eye-witness report from the year 1904.
Many articles in the world's press furnish unequivocal proof that the Telemobiloscope was the forerunner of today's radar, as do the issued Patent documents:

British Patent No. 13170 of 10 June 1904

A Hertzian Wave Projecting and Receiving Apparatus Adapted to Indicate or Give Warning of the Presence of a Metallic Body, such as a Ship or a Train, in the Line of Projection of such Waves.

and:

British Patent No. 24608 of 24 November 1904

Improvements in Hertzian Wave Projecting and Receiving Apparatus for Locating the Position of Distant Metal Objects.

which were awarded to the applicant as the first discoverer of radar.

It should not be difficult for you to obtain the above-mentioned documents for your examination and to satisfy yourself of the accuracy of my statements.

Today the discoverer, Engineer Christian Hülsmeyer, is already 70 years old and lives in Düsseldorf. In those days he was very much before his time and found, on account of his youth (23 years old) neither comprehension nor support for his discovery.

I am sure you will not refuse the implementation of an absolutely impartial investigation, and give to a German his due esteem and recognition.

Very respectfully yours,
Your obedient servant,
Erich Hecker

Presumably, the clerk at the Patent Office suffered from poor eyesight. The reply was as cold as it was illogical:

The Patent Office
25, Southampton Buildings
London, W.C.2.
3rd April 1951

Sir,

I am directed by the Comptroller to thank you for your letter of the 5th March and for the information contained therein, and to say that he regrets that the matter raised is not one on which he is empowered to take any action.

I should add, however, that in this country the term 'Radar' is used to denote a system which includes means for determining the position of the distant object, that is, the distance thereof from the observer.

I am, Sir,
Your obedient Servant,
A.V. King.

Obedient to whom, one wonders? Since Hülsmeyer's system most certainly included means for 'determining the position of the distant object', it is debatable whether the old-fashioned notion of British fair play counts for very much ... Even Sir Robert Watson-Watt himself, on meeting Hülsmeyer at an International Radar Conference in 1954 in Germany, seems to have missed the point: '...even my long-awaited meeting with Christian Hülsmeyer, who was introduced to me as "the father of radar", could not cure me of the queer conviction that one parent was enough even for the lustiest of infants.'[1]

At least Hülsmeyer had the satisfaction of receiving honour in his own country where scientists and politicians plied him with distinction, and where a street and a square in Düsseldorf are named after him, together with a modern Army barracks near his home town of Eydelstedt. Rather meagre compensation though for a discovery which, if taken up at the time, might have changed world history.

---

[1] *Three Steps to Victory*. Robert Watson-Watt, Odham's, London, 1957.

CHAPTER TWO

The Developments of the Thirties

With the exception of a paper by the engineer Loewy which outlined the broad principle of reflection techniques but was never backed up by practical trials, radiolocation ideas remained dormant in Germany until the beginning of the First World War.[1] Their resurrection was the brainchild of Richard Scherl, son of a newspaper magnate, who discussed the idea with his friend the engineer and author Hans Dominik. Impressed, Dominik designed a transmitter and receiver operating on 10 cm and called the system a *Strahlenzieler* or 'Beam-Aimer' and offered it to Siemens and Halske for development. Owing to the pressures of war work they turned it down, though one of their directors, Hans Fielder, the inventor of the flame-thrower, was impressed enough to offer his financial and moral support for the development of an improved model.

In February 1916 Dominik approached the German Navy with reports of his tests, and though they showed interest they also pointed out that a further six months' developmental work was needed before it could go into service. At this time the Navy was going through a bad patch and said in effect, 'With this war, and the time factor involved, it's out of the question.' And while Fielder backed the venture right up to the end of the war further progress was never made.

---

[1] The principles of reflecting wave technology were well known to researchers at this time and were featured in many physics textbooks and laboratory experiments. Scherl's idea was of course based on them, as was the work of more well known researchers such as Nikola Tesla who carried out similar experiments at Colorado Springs. It is of course possible that many others had similar ideas at this time but which failed to attract much attention.

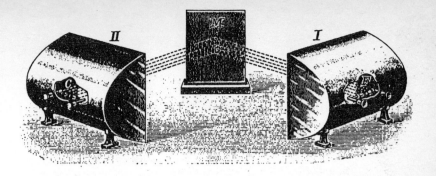

'If the pair of reflectors are placed at an angle as shown, the coherer will not operate until the metal plate 'M' is so positioned that the electric rays from reflector 1 are reflected from the plate to reflector 2. The electric waves behave similarly to light waves.'

Figure 4 Centimetre wave research, on 10 cm, in 1913! A diagram from a physics textbook by L. Graetz (*Fritz Trenkle*).

Between 1922 and 1923 Loewy turned his hand to experimental radio altimeters for aircraft and discovered that the change in capacity between the ground and his antennas varied according to the geological features of the earth, and though he thought this might be useful for geological exploration nothing came of the idea.

Worldwide research into the ionosphere was conducted on a large scale from the mid-twenties onwards, and pulse techniques pioneered by Breit and Tuve in America enabled Professor E.V. Appleton in Britain to determine the height of the Heaviside Layer, while at the same time radio technology made great advances. In 1922 Taylor and Young at the United States Naval Research Laboratory carried out experiments on 5 metres and succeeded in detecting a small steamer at a few hundred yards. Subsequent increases in range following further experiments led to a report being submitted to the appropriate authorities who promptly filed and forgot it, and much the same thing happened in 1931 to the 50 cm pulse system for detecting ships devised by A.S. Butement and P.E. Pollard of the Signals Experimental Station at Woolwich.[1]

That the ground had been prepared for the emergence of modern radar at this time is attested by the late Sir Robert Watson-Watt's '...it could have happened any time after 1926.'[2]

[1] Obviously much more research was carried out between World War I and the thirties, but there is not the space to devote to it here. A fairly comprehensive review of such activities is to be found in Sir Robert Watson-Watt's *Three Steps to Victory*.

[2] *Three Steps to Victory*, op cit.

A statement with small consolation for those who found their efforts to be of lesser significance than his own, even taking into account the stimulus of the threat of war. And while it is true that most countries can point to some experimentation into near-radar techniques at this time, Germany alone was the first to produce the earliest practical systems.

In 1929, six years before Watson-Watt's Daventry Experiment, Dr Rudolf Kühnhold, Scientific Liaison Officer in the Civil Service Department of the German Navy's Communications Research Establishment at Kiel, conducted experiments into the design of a depth-sounder working in both the vertical and horizontal planes which determined depth and range very accurately by twin receiving systems working on a rotating principle. It occurred to him that this principle might be employed for the detection of surface craft by using centimetric wavelengths, and that the location of aircraft might also be possible.

The stimulus for this idea was precisely the same one that later prompted the British Air Ministry to form a committee to investigate methods of aircraft detection other than the sound locators then in current use, for Kühnhold knew very well that sound locators had little future due to the increasing speed of aircraft which, in a worsening ratio to the given constants of the speed of sound, would soon render them unreliable. On his initiative, therefore, the Research Establishment ordered a transmitter and receiver working on 13.5 cm from the Pintsch Company. The transmitter worked on the Barkhausen-Kurz principle of oscillation and its output of 100 mw of continuous waves was fed to compact directional antennas, tone modulation being employed to ensure echoes were audible above the receiver noise. The *Bremsröhren* valves of both transmitter and receiver were placed respectively at the focal points of two 80 cm diameter reflectors mounted side by side, but when these were directed towards a ship in Kiel Harbour only poor results were obtained. Clearly, greater power was called for and this presented difficulties.

The problem of generating high power on centimetric wavelengths had occupied engineering thought for some time, and apart from the experimental magnetrons designed by Hull of the General Electric Company of America, Habaan and Yagi of Japan and Zacek of Czechoslovakia, all of which delivered only minute powers,[1] only two methods were known: the

[1] These were the principal researchers up to 1929. Later contributors to

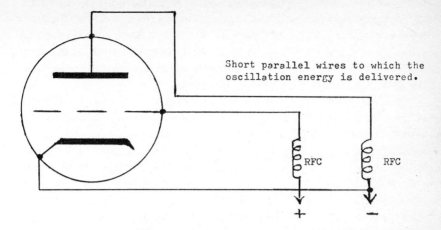

Short parallel wires to which the
oscillation energy is delivered.

RFC   RFC

+   −

The triode shown here is operated with the grid at a positive potential and the anode at a small negative potential. Electrons emitted from the cathode are attracted to the grid but most of them pass through the grid structure into the space between the grid and the anode where they slow down and stop just before reaching the anode. The electrons are then drawn back towards the grid with increasing velocity and, if not captured by the grid structure, pass on into the space between the grid and cathode and slow down just before reaching it. This oscillation around the grid is repeated many times before an electron ultimately escapes from the valve into the associated circuitry by a chance collison against the grid structure, the frequency of which is determined by the construction of the valve and the grid potential. The 'braking' or retarding features exhibited between grid and anode and grid and cathode are characteristics of the valve employed, which was known to the Germans as the *Bremsröhre*, or 'Retarding-field' valve.

Figure 5 The Barkhausen-Kurz principle of generating centimetric wavelengths (*Fritz Trenkle*).

old-fashioned spark gap which could be adjusted to the required frequency, and the Barkhausen-Kurz oscillator which could be 'squeezed' to a wavelength of about 10 cm. A possible reason for the absence of conventional valves of useful power may have been due to conclusions drawn by the engineering world as instanced by Professor R.V. Jones:

> ...there was a doctrine that radio wavelengths of the order of 10 centimetres could not be generated by electronic valves because the time taken by the electrons to pass through the valve was much too great. This argument was fallacious, but was accepted by many scientists and engineers because we had become almost congenitally inclined to accept such 'postulates of impotence' in basic science ... I came myself to see the fallacy in the argument about the impossibility of generating centimetric waves. It arose from a demonstration at Farnborough of a very powerful loudspeaker system and

magnetron development are dealt with in Sir Robert Watson-Watt's *Three Steps to Victory*.

amplifying system that had been developed for installation in aircraft policing the North-West frontier of India. This policing was sometimes done by punishing marauding tribesmen by bombing their villages, after due warning. Someone thought that the warning would be all the more effective if it came as from the voice of God, bellowing out from an aircraft. When the apparatus had been perfected, it was demonstrated to the Air Staff at Farnborough by mounting a microphone on one side of the aerodrome, some two thousand feet away. If you spoke into the microphone you could hear your voice coming two seconds later across from the other side. All went well with the demonstration until one of the inspecting officers struck by the curiosity of hearing his delayed voice, started to laugh. Two seconds later there came back a laugh from the loudspeaker at which everybody laughed. Two seconds later the shower of laughter returned, and I like to think that by now the volume was so great that the returned laugh was picked up by the microphone and duly relayed once again, making a system that laughed by itself.

Apart from the comedy of the situation, there was an important lesson to be learnt. This was that the time of oscillations generated by the human voice is typically of the order of one thousandth of a second, and yet these were being faithfully generated by a system in which the transit time of sound across the aerodrome was some two seconds. This showed the fallacy in the argument about centimetric waves. What really mattered was not the transit time itself, but the regularity in the time of transit. So if electrons could be persuaded to travel at uniform speeds across the valve they could be made to generate oscillations of considerably shorter period and wavelength than the limit which the previous careless theory had predicted.[1]

Presumably this 'careless theory' had more effect on the German valve manufacturers than on the Dutch, for in spite of Kühnhold's demands for high-power versions no German help was forthcoming, but shortly after his first experiment Philips of Holland developed a magnetron which, in a push-pull stage, generated 80 watts on 13 cm. Pintsch designed the next transmitter around these valves, still using continuous waves and a 1000 Hz modulation tone, but as the push-pull method

---

[1] *Most Secret War*, Hamish Hamilton, 1978. All following quotations from Professor R.V. Jones are from the same source unless otherwise stated.

proved unstable they had to be content with a single-ended stage delivering only 40 watts. Nevertheless, when Yagi antennas were employed, much better results were obtained. The receiver was much the same, but it now incorporated an improved low-frequency amplifier and a single dipole as an antenna. Tests over Kiel Harbour gave ranges of up to 2 or 3 kilometres.

Financing of the research was undertaken not by Kühnhold's own Department but by the Torpedo Research Establishment who were in urgent need of accurate range data for their new weapons, and it was for this reason that the determination of sea targets was then the greatest priority. From this it can be seen how the German radar requirement, at least at first, differed from the British. Britain, from the mid-thirties, faced an ever-growing threat from German air superiority, and in view of the weakened state of the RAF and the increasing number of standing patrols which would be needed to intercept the enemy, a more efficient method of detection was required than the existing sound locators. For this reason Sir Henry Tizard's Committee approached Watson-Watt for help in 1935.

German military philosophy at this time was one of attack, strike and destroy. Defensive methods in the sense of the British requirement were not foreseen, at least not on a similar scale, and in any case the relationships between German industry and the Services were different from those existing between the British Armed Forces and their scientists, as Jones points out:

It appeared to us that at the beginning of the war the Germans had not thought nearly so much about the use of radar as we had ourselves ... The difference could be explained by our having thought almost entirely defensively whilst they were giving priority to offensive action. As a result in Britain, the serving officers and the scientists and engineers had been thrown much more together by the bombing threat, and had thus come to appreciate one another's problems much more than did their German counterparts ... The Germans, by contrast, did not have the same close relationship between their serving officers and their scientists. When radar became a technical possibility the German Services drew up specifications which the scientists and engineers then tried to satisfy. And very well they did so, within the limits imposed by the specifications. German radar was much better engineered than ours, it was much more like a scientific instrument in stability and precision of performance. The philosophy of using it, however, seemed to have been left to the German Services, and the Luftwaffe in particular made a philosophical mistake by focusing on the wrong objective.

The limited finances of the Torpedo Research Department in the early thirties led them to seek out firms willing to undertake Kühnhold's experimental work at an economic figure, and one of the first to be approached was the Tonographie Company, but they were unwilling to abandon their work on sonar systems for the Communications Research Establishment in which more profit could be made for something which promised less. Similar reasons were advanced by other firms, and as the expansion of the programme was considered essential it was decided to go cap in hand to Telefunken and sound them out. Accordingly, on an impulse, Kühnhold drove down to Berlin and, without seeking an appointment, demanded to see Dr Wilhelm Runge. The accounts of this meeting by both men are illuminating. According to Kühnhold:

> Obviously there were many contacts between myself and the various specialist firms. The active participation of these in the Naval Research Programme was however difficult if not impossible because the capacity of these firms was already taken up since the outbreak of war.

A somewhat puzzling statement since most of these contacts were made long before the war.

> So, for example, the Telefunken Company was committed to 80% of their production for the Luftwaffe and 20% for the Army. And despite the reports in various publications that not very good personal relations existed between myself and Dr Runge, no role was played by Telefunken in radar development for the Navy because they never were employed in this respect.

Even more puzzling, since Telefunken turned out a great deal of work for the Navy, as these pages will show.[1]

---

[1] If there seems to be confusion here it should be explained that Telefunken's work was (at first) carried out under licence. The contacts with specialist firms obviously began before the outbreak of war and in fact continued throughout it, but the main problem at the beginning was to interest them in the early radar programme and to get them to carry out the work at an economic figure. It should also be borne in mind that most of the major electronics companies were already committed to other urgent and, in some cases, more lucrative pursuits.

As far as the Navy was concerned, the main active firms were Elac of Kiel and the Atlas-Werke of Bremen, and even they were engaged in other fields of radio technology with little room to spare for our developing radar programme. For this reason Admiral Mertens went ahead with the founding of the Navy-sponsored Gema Company.[1]

Since Dr Runge throws more light on these 'not very good personal relations' in the next chapter, it is convenient to leave the subject for the moment. But in fairness to Kühnhold it is only right to point out that it was on his own initiative that the Gema Company was founded, yet at the same time he also obtained financial help outside his own department, namely the Artillery, which enabled him to set up and equip a radar research station at Pelzerhaken under the control of the Communications Research Establishment. Kühnhold visited the station twice a week to discuss scientific and technical problems, but at the same time he found himself plunged in other matters. Internal difficulties plagued the new station in these early days, chiefly because its new director was not equal to the developmental tasks and the new equipment, to say nothing of his problems in co-operating with scientists in industry. He was, in any case, replaced by Dr G. Röhrl in 1936. Kühnhold's own account of this period is interesting:

Since the beginning of the war in 1939 a very unequal contest developed between the Luftwaffe and the Navy in the field of radiolocation and the corresponding construction of equipment. The Luftwaffe understood it through better relationships with Goering that the expert firms had a better research and production capacity and the Navy, for this reason, was constantly discriminated against, until it succeeded on the occasion of a weapon demonstration at Eckenförde in 1938 in the presence of Hitler, Göring, Admiral Raeder and others of the leadership to draw attention to the particular work of the Navy in the field of radiolocation and its significant results.

The Pelzerhaken branch of the Communications Research Establishment conducted both scientific and practical research work with a preponderance of civilian personnel. In the first half of 1930 there were three working groups of two or three scientists and the same number of engineers. During

[1] Gesellschaft für Elektroakustische und Mechanische Apparate (company for electro-acoustical and mechanical apparatus).

the thirties the department became more established, and at the outbreak of war, on the direction of the Naval High Command in Berlin, I took on in addition a number of university professors for the reinforcement of the scientific personnel, particularly in the field of radiolocation. I must add that the decision of the High Command to do this was without consultation with myself, for I was rather of the opinion that these scientists in their own university laboratories were of greater use to the Navy there than at Pelzerhaken, as there was not enough working space for them to conduct their own researches. Fortunately, I was able to convince Rear-Admiral Mertens at the High Command of these problems and in the event the professors were returned to their universities. Mertens held a responsible post in Naval Communications in Berlin before becoming the Head of the Communications Research Establishment in 1942. He was a highly qualified officer and had commanded a U-boat in the First World War. It was Mertens who was responsible for putting forward my idea of the formation of the Gema Company under the later directorship of Dr Willisen and Herr Erbslöh and to relieve me of the corresponding specialist assignments outside the Communications Research Establishment, and as a result of the simpler financial settlement the running costs could be authorised.

While Pintsch persevered with the 13.5 cm design Gema had other ideas, and a team under the lively direction of Dr Schultes immediately raised the wavelength to 48 cm and provided the receiver with Yagi antennas in a 1.5 metre diameter paraboloid. This was clearly a step in the right direction because trials against the vessel *Hessen*[1] in Kiel Harbour immediately overloaded the receiver, and while modifications were made it was also decided to use pulse operation for the transmitter and to incorporate cathode-ray tubes for range finding through pulse timing. With these improvements Gema felt sure that the relatively small costs incurred would enable returns to be received without the problems of stray radiation.

Pintsch, on the other hand, improved the 13.5 cm system and increased the power to 300 milliwatts. They discovered this wavelength to be much better when beamed over land than

---

[1] 13,200 tons. Taken over by the Reichsmarine in 1925 and converted to a radio controlled target ship 1936-37.

over water, for on 15 May 1934 trials against the research vessel *Welle* (formerly the *Grille*) resulted in perfect detection of the modulated tone at about 2 km, while experiments carried out on the island of Wangerooge gave even better results.

Faced with this Gema was spurred to greater efforts, and after improving the screening of their equipment and employing a *Tannenbaum* (Christmas tree) antenna to reduce even further the stray radiation, an even better result was confidently expected, but in the event they only managed about 300 metres.

The situation now carried the hallmarks of a contest between the two firms and Gema was determined not to be beaten. After a deal of discussion among their staff followed by even greater efforts, they managed to increase the range to 2 and later 4 km. They had not been slow to notice that Pintsch's equipment produced a greater echo slope from the target, and not to be outdone they went ahead and built their magnetron into another paraboloid with a diameter equal to 5 wavelengths and employed two receivers: one a super-regenerative system and the other a superhet with an intermediate frequency of 1.6 MHz, both being placed 200 metres from the transmitter to reduce stray fields and false returns.

On 24 October 1934 tests gave a range of 12 km against the *Welle*, with an additional bonus of a return from a Junkers W34 which chanced to fly across the beam at 700 metres. A representative of the Torpedo Research Establishment who had been invited to the demonstration was so impressed that he enabled a further research grant of 70,000 Reichmarks (about £10,000)[1] to be awarded. At the same time it was ordered that all future research should be subject to secrecy and that development should proceed on the following lines:

(a) Pulse operation of transmitters to achieve longer ranges. (Owing to the short pulse duration the valves could be considerably over-rated)

(b) Receiver muting during transmission.

(c) Development of range measurement techniques by the timing of the pulses on cathode-ray tubes (crt).

(d) Development of sense direction-finding methods through switching of the antenna direction. (A/N bearings)

(e) Development of centimetric triodes for receivers and magnetrons for transmitters for operation over a wide frequency range.

(f) Concentration on a frequency of 600 MHz (50 cm).

---

[1] At the exchange rate of those times.

Despite these orders Gema continued for a time to use continuous waves, and a few weeks later located a seaplane at 12 km.

By May 1935, barely a few weeks after Watson-Watt's celebrated Daventry Experiment,[1] Gema had developed a new transmitter for the required pulse techniques which generated 800 watts at a Pulse-Rate Frequency (prf) of 2,000 Hz and a pulse duration of 2 microseconds. A greater range was immediately attained and by the use of phase-conversion the echoes could be observed and the ranges measured on a crt. The antenna system was a *Tannenbaum* array consisting of ten pairs of dipoles against a wire mesh reflector, and the receiver was an improved super-regenerative model employing American 'Acorn' valves, the receiving antenna being a smaller *Tannenbaum* with only three pairs of dipoles and a mesh reflector. Early trials proved the screening to be so good that both transmitting and receiving antennas could be mounted side by side, which was a decided operational advantage. Returns from the opposite side of a wooded bay were outstanding.

Trials against the *Welle* were, however, disappointing since ranges of only about 4 km were achieved, but they proved the efficiency of the range measurement principle. This was obtained through a vertical deflection of the X-axis of both the transmitting and receiving antennas whereupon the transmitted pulse was displayed on the screen as a large trace and the corresponding echo shown at the appropriate position

[1] British radar came into existence only after A.P. Rowe, assistant to the Directorate of Scientific Research at the Air Ministry, discovered in mid 1934 that the existing sound locators were virtually useless for early warning purposes. He brought this to the attention of his chief, H.E. Wimperis, who in turn urged Lord Londonderry, Secretary of State for Air, to set up a committee to find new methods of air defence. The Committee for the Scientific Survey of Air Defence was inaugurated in November 1934 under the chairmanship of Sir Henry Tizard, with Professor A.V. Hill and Professor P.M.S. Blackett as members and Rowe as secretary. The first meeting was on 28 January 1935, when Watson-Watt was asked to submit a paper on the detection of aircraft by radio methods. On 14 February Watson-Watt delivered a paper *The Detection and Location of Aircraft by Radio Methods* and was asked for a practical demonstration. This was carried out on 26 February when a Heyford bomber piloted by Squadron Leader R.S. Blucke flew through the beam of the BBC Daventry transmitter while Watson-Watt and his team watched the results on an oscilloscope connected to a receiver. This successful demonstration, known henceforth as the Daventry Experiment, led to the setting up of a research station at Orfordness, and later at Bawdsey Manor near Felixstowe. In March 1936 a 240-foot tower enabled them to detect an aircraft at seventy-five miles.

along the horizontal timebase line, where it was seen against a measurement scale, thus making range measurement quite accurate. But the experiments also confirmed that the high frequencies employed introduced a slight declivity of the echo which, small as it was, did not conform to the standards of precision demanded. After much deliberation Gema made a decision which was to lead to one of the most useful radar systems Germany possessed, for they went ahead with a similar developmental equipment but changed the frequency to 125 MHz.

It was at this point that arguments arose between those in favour of abandoning the 48 cm system and those wishing to persevere with it, and Dr Willisen settled the matter by deciding in favour of both. So as development of the 125 MHz equipment took place, another group continued on 48 cm, and despite strong security prohibitions carried out trials against the cruiser *Königsberg* by means of a ruse, when they attained ranges up to 8 km. During these tests the phenomenon of 'Aspect of Bearing' was observed, and it was found that the antennas had to be slightly reorientated from the point of maximum bearing, a similar effect having been reported by Taylor and Young several years earlier.

During this period an urgent demand was made of the rest of German industry for improved and smaller crt's as those in current use were not always reliable.

By September the 48 cm group had made much headway and felt confident enough to demonstrate their improved equipment to senior naval representatives, when the gunnery instruction ship *Bremse* was located with a bearing accuracy of $\pm0.15°$ at about 15 km. Realising they had the makings of a superb tactical weapon within their grasp, the Naval High Command made additional research funds available and laid down that further security measures would be introduced. From now on German radar was to be disguised under the name *Dezimeter Telegraphie* or *De-Te* for short, and during the following year even more designations appeared, most of which were abbreviations of *Funkmessgeräte* (Radio Measuring Apparatus) or *Funkmessortungsgeräte* (Radio Locating Apparatus) and appeared as *FmG*, *FuMG* or *FuMO* according to the branch of the armed forces employing the equipment.

Faced with greater responsibility Gema now pushed ahead with a quicker development of a pulse triode for their 48 cm radar, while work on the 125 MHz system continued apace. But the development of the triode required that the equipment should be transported to Berlin, and before they did so, they carried out a further test by installing it in the *Welle* for trials against land targets when ranges up to 20 km were easily attained, though other ships could be located only to about 7 km, and while this proved the value of shipboard radar it was clear that longer ranges were required. The group was reluctant to change the working frequency in view of its successes, and it was only after much insistence by Dr Willisen that they were persuaded to design the equipment for 82 cm when, according to Willisen, improved valve efficiency would obviously lengthen the range. When the group declared that the new pulse triode would do this very well on 48 cm, Willisen retorted that in that case it would work even better on the frequency he suggested, and eventually he was conceded the victory. This and further improvements led to the series of naval radars known by several different names but under the general classification of *Seetakt*.

By February 1936 Gema produced the first model of the 125 MHz equipment. They had succeeded in developing a triode with a pulse power of 8 kW, and the new receiver, a superhet, used 'Acorn' valves in the input stage. Yagi antennas were still employed but during tests it was found that they were incorrectly positioned and were producing a too high radiation pattern because they failed to detect the vessel at which they were directed and instead located an aircraft at 8 km. The following day the group once more adjusted the antennas and this time tracked an aircraft out to 28 km, and after they reported this to the Communications Research Establishment a great deal of high level discussion took place (in which Kühnhold had much to say) when it was decided to use the equipment as an early-warning radar for aircraft in place of the original intention of its employment against ships. Accordingly, the transmitter was rebuilt with a push-pull power amplifier and the receiver sensitivity further improved, while the *Tannenbaum* array was replaced with a system of stacked dipoles. This was the forerunner of the series known as *Freya*.

In this year two other firms entered the radar scene and began producing results. Without official invitation the valve laboratories of the Lorenz Company, under the energetic direction of Dr Herringer, developed new 'Acorn' valves as well as high power transmitting valves for their own radar research, which also concentrated on centimetric wavelengths. At the same time Telefunken began manufacturing similar valves and was also taking an interest in radar technology.

Lorenz, however, developed excellent antenna systems and attained much better receiver sensitivity which, with higher transmitting power, led in a very short time to superior target-tracking and ranging. And while technical problems of using centimetres had still to be overcome, they installed their first equipment on the roofs of their Berlin laboratory at the beginning of the year and enjoyed a certain degree of success. The transmitter differed from conventional equipment in that it employed a thyratron delivering 400 watts of pulse power, an obvious advantage over the customary valves which would have consumed vast quantities of energy. Early ranges were about 15 km using a prf of 10 kHz, and the receiver was a super-regenerative type with greatly increased sensitivity. For antennas a stacked array known as the 'mattress' enabled the Berlin Cathedral to be consistently located at a range of 7.4 km.

Later in the year Lorenz introduced a new transmitting valve, the DS 320, which delivered 1 kW of pulse power with a 1 microsecond pulse duration, and the receiver was replaced with a superhet using a self-oscillating mixer stage from a fully regulated power supply. These refinements increased the range to 14 km, and during tests the team observed an interesting phenomenon when they directed the antennas at a revolving windmill sail, for further experiments into the curious echoes received led to the principle of Propeller Modulation which was put to good use during the war.

The equipment had been designed to be transportable, and by the autumn it was installed in naval ships and located other vessels at ranges up to 8 km, and on one occasion a Junkers W34 at 4 km. (To say nothing of flocks of birds that plagued it incessantly.)

Lorenz were actually in an awkward position as far as the official German radar programme was concerned, for they had more commitments in the international market than other firms. Their Blind Landing System, for example, was even then employed by the RAF under licence, and though they were looked upon as a security risk by the High Command, they forged ahead with their own radar development confident that some time in the near future the customers would turn up. On their own initiative, therefore, they improved the equipment still further by changing the frequency to 62.4 MHz and used parabolic reflectors with a diameter of 2.4 metres, and when the prf was changed to 5 kHz a range of 30 km was reached. The introduction of circuitry which produced a circular time-base pattern on the screen, within which the echo traces were deflected to indicate range, improved it even more. The antennas were specially designed to maintain a range of 30 km despite severe weather conditions, and it was these that prompted General Wolfgang Martini, Head of Luftwaffe Signals, not only to take an interest in the firm's work, but also to enter into an 'unofficial' agreement with them. Indeed, Martini's influence was such that he was able to bring about an even more 'unofficial' understanding with Lorenz so that they were eventually commissioned to develop an anti-aircraft gunnery radar, later known as the *A2-Gerät*, which employed the same 'weather independent' antennas with adjustable height and bearing controls.

While this was taking place other new establishments were formed. The most important of these being the Drahtlos-Luftelektrisch Versuchsgesellschaft Gräfeling (the DVG) (Wireless Air-electric Research Company, Gräfeling, near Munich) which carried out research, particularly into high frequency valves, together with a subsidiary department the Flugfunkforschungsinstitut (Air Radio Research Institute) (the FFO) at Oberpfaffenhofen under the direction of Professor Max Dieckmann. These centres were formed in 1935 and a great deal of research was carried out into Doppler-Effect techniques using continuous-wave transmitters on 10 and 5 centimetres. Useful results were obtained from experiments on the Ammersee Lake near Munich where speed measurements of passing steamers were taken with reasonable accuracy, although actual figures are no longer available. The original 13.5 cm work was also continued.[1]

At about this time an account was widely circulated among some technical quarters (and believed by many even today) that a certain Professor Gubeau and his colleague Professor Zenneck at Munich had developed a small radar system which could be installed in a car. Two parabolic reflectors, one above the other, were mounted on the rear, and the range claimed was between 10 and 100 metres, but details about this are not known because the men were granted a 'secret patent' which they promptly put in a safe so that its circuitry and operation could never be revealed ...

Also in 1936 the High Command decided it was time to look at development trends and lay down further requirements. After a deal of consultation it was announced that early

---

[1] Although it never led to a radar device on this wavelength. It did, however, pave the way for further experimental work on centimetres generally.

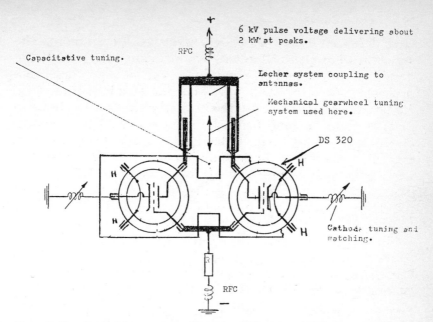

Capacitative tuning.

RFC

6 kV pulse voltage delivering about 2 kW' at peaks.

Lecher system coupling to antennas.

Mechanical gearwheel tuning system used here.

DS 320

Cathode tuning and matching.

RFC

Figure 6 The circuit of the power amplifier stage of the Lorenz *FMG 38 L* (used in their Berlin experiments) employing the DS320 pulse triode (*Fritz Trenkle*).

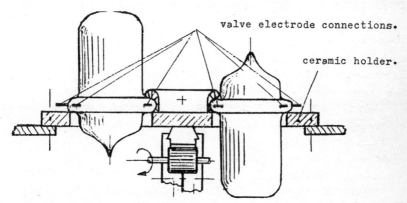

valve electrode connections.

ceramic holder.

Pair of DS320 pulse triodes in push-pull, delivering a pulse power of 1 kW on 480 MHz (62.4 cm). Cooling by convection.

Figure 7 Physical arrangement of the power amplifier stage of the *FMG (Flak) 38 L Kurfürst* (*Fritz Trenkle*).

warning radar should be capable of ranges up to 50 km and heights of 2,000 metres, with a range measurement accuracy of at least 10 metres. At the same time Flak radar should have a range of at least 25 km and a range measurement accuracy of 10 metres, with a height and bearing accuracy of one sixteenth of a degree. Flak equipment was also to be provided with IFF (Identification Friend or Foe) systems to work automatically with the measuring devices. The Army Weapons Department,

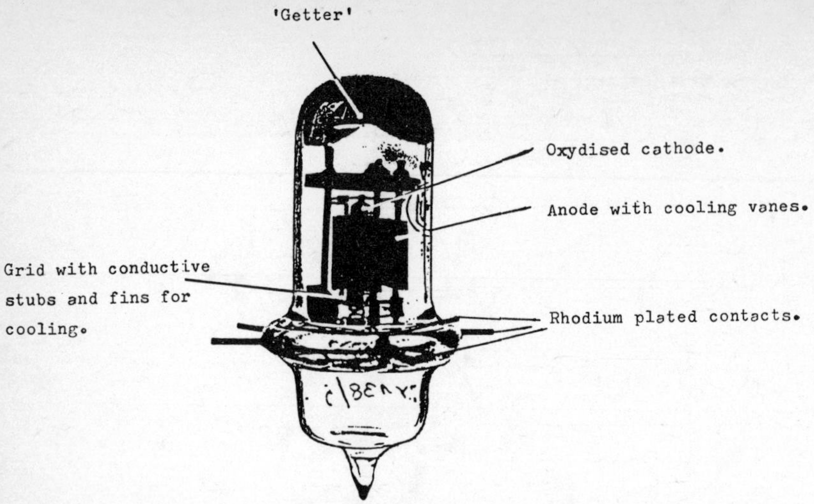

'Getter'

Oxydised cathode.

Anode with cooling vanes.

Grid with conductive
stubs and fins for
cooling.

Rhodium plated contacts.

Figure 8 The first laboratory model of the DS320 pulse triode by Lorenz (*Fritz Trenkle*).

who were responsible at this time for translating the wishes of
the High Command into actions, took the matter up with both
Lorenz and Telefunken, and as by now Lorenz were well on
their way with their *A2-Gerät* and weatherproof antenna
systems, it was decided to test it at the Forward Command
Anti-Aircraft Training School at Lynow, where it passed with
flying colours and was accepted into service under the
designation *FmG (Flak) 38 L Kurfürst* (Elector, or electoral
prince).

A clever feature of this model was the employment of the
carriage and barrel of the 88 mm Flak gun, the carriage
supporting the main equipment while the barrel, raised to a
vertical position, became the column for supporting the retractable rotating mast which carried two parabolic reflectors each
of 2.4 metres diameter mounted one above the other. These
could be rotated to maximum bearing and height and could
easily detect the changing azimuth and elevation angles of
aircraft, while efficient weatherproofing of the main equipment
and operating console ensured efficient and comfortable conditions for its crew. The screen incorporated an engraved scale
reading from 0 to 30 km and the echo traces, as mentioned,
were read off from a circular time-base representation. The
Kurfürst operated on 480 MHz (62.4 cm) with a pulse power of 1
kW and an average range reliability of 12 km, range
measurement accuracy being about 100 metres with a bearing
accuracy of 3°. Antenna rotation was motorised, but manual
operation was also possible. As a result of the excellent tests
Lorenz received an order from the Flak for 20 sets.

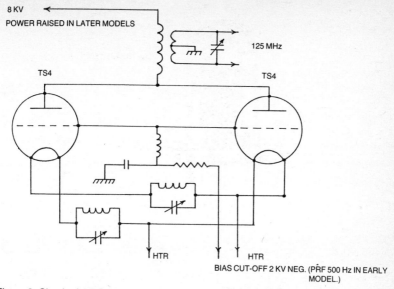

Figure 9 Circuit of the *Freya* power amplifier, *circa* 1936 (*Fritz Trenkle*.)

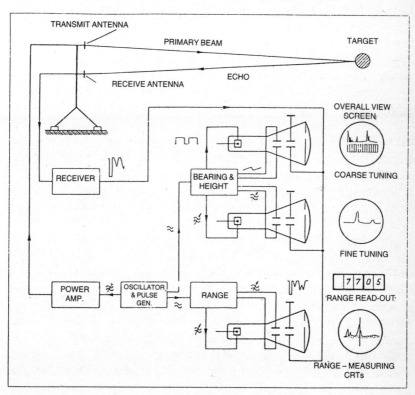

Figure 10 Block layout of the *Freya* radar, 1939-40 (*Fritz Trenkle*).

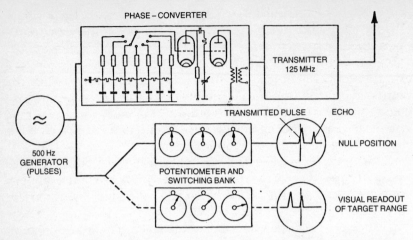

Figure 11 The range-finding method of *Freya*, circa 1939-40. Height and bearing are determined by antenna angle and direction, and both are displayed on CRTs (*Fritz Trenkle*).

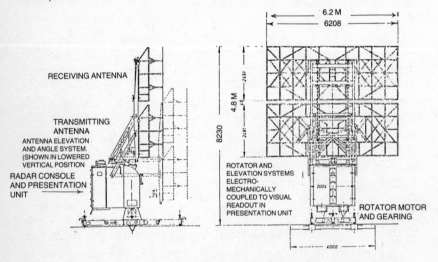

Figure 12 Side and rear view of the *Freya* antenna in the working position (*Fritz Trenkle*).

As far as the early warning requirement was concerned, Gema had now improved their 125 MHz radar to the point where it was ready for official trials, and on 15 November 1938 it was tested at Lynow under the code-name *A1 Gerät Freya*. It now used a low-frequency generator to produce a sinusoidal waveform on 2 KHz which was fed over an adjustable phase-conversion circuit to the deflection plates of a pair of crt's, and then by further conversion and amplification to provide the bias voltage for the grids of the power amplifier valves, thus generating the pulses. The receiver output was coupled to the vertical deflection plates so that the echo trace was displayed further along the horizontal time-base line at a corresponding distance from the larger trace of the transmitted pulse. Height, bearing and range were read from three screens, one giving an overall quick view of the total 75 km range, while the others were for fine measurements, an additional refinement being the provision of a roller-counter (an early form of digital read-out) electro-mechanically coupled to the phase-conversion unit for instant range evaluation.

This early *Freya* delivered 8 kW of pulse power on 125 MHz with a *Tannenbaum* array of transmitting and receiving antennas stacked one above the other which gave a range, dependent on the target height, of between 40 and 75 km with a range measurement accuracy of 2 km and a bearing accuracy of about 5°. The operating cabin with its antenna array was rotated either electrically or mechanically, and the whole equipment could be easily dismantled for transportation.[1]

*

In 1935 British radar development began with great secrecy under the volcanic direction of Watson-Watt, who had been approached for help by Sir Henry Tizard's Committee for the Scientific Survey of Air Defence. At that time the British could not have known that German radar had got off to a fair start a few years earlier. In fact by 1939 they still had little idea of what the Germans might be up to in the field of scientific warfare, and thought it would be sensible to engage a scientist to try and find out, and possibly recommend measures to improve the flow of information.

Accordingly, A.E. Woodward-Nutt, Secretary of the Committee, paid a visit to Dr R.V. Jones, a scientist in the Admiralty

[1] It will be noticed that the *Freya's* frequency of 125 MHz was considerably lower than most of the other German systems, which were mainly in the centimetric region. Its beamwidth of about 40° and excellent receiver sensitivity made it very suitable for its task as an early-warning radar. The British early-warning system, the *Chain Home*, worked on 12 metres using transmitting towers 360 feet high and with very high power. This resulted in a 'floodlit' area stretching for about 120 miles (sometimes even more) with an angle of approximately 120°, and showed every aircraft in its beam. There were, however, gaps in the system. It was possible for aircraft to fly below the beam undetected, and for this reason radar equipments known as the *Chain Home Low* were employed to find them. These operated on 200 MHz with rotating antennas and had a range of approximately 80 miles. The Germans generally concentrated on centimetric wavelengths which, by virtue of their 'line of sight' characteristics, resulted in a much narrower beam. And while this brought about greater accuracy it meant that a greater number of equipments were required to cover their defences.

Research Laboratory at Teddington, who accepted the post
with alacrity and was given a room at the Headquarters of MI6
at 54, Broadway.[1]

A few weeks later a mysterious parcel appeared on his desk.
This came from a 'friendly German scientist' who had put a
letter through the door of the British Naval Attaché in Oslo
saying that if the British wished to learn about certain German
scientific projects they had only to change their introduction to
their news broadcasts in German in such a way that the sender
would know his information was welcome.

On opening the parcel Jones was astonished to find
revelations about several German systems (all of which were to
make their appearance during the course of the war) but one
paragraph was of immediate interest:

> It told us that in the raid by Bomber Command on
> Wilhelmshafen in September (1939) our aircraft had been
> detected at a range of 120 km by radar stations with an
> output of 20 kW. It did not state the wavelength, but
> suggested that we should find this for ourselves and jam the
> transmissions. There was another radar system using
> paraboloid aerials and operating on wavelengths of around
> 50 centimetres.

The 'Oslo Report', as it was known, was not taken seriously by the
three Service Ministries. Jones, they pointed out, was an
'innocent in Intelligence work' and the whole thing was a
disinformation exercise. Nevertheless, as the war progressed
everything in it came to pass, and during the 'duller days of the
war' Jones would often look it up 'to see what was coming next'.
The identity of the author has never been revealed, though
Jones believes he knows it but chooses to keep it to himself 'in case
the author's family should suffer any neo-Nazi persecution'.[2]

---

[1] Technically, Professor (then Dr) Jones had been attached to the Air
Ministry Staff from 1936 while he was still conducting infra-red research at
the Clarendon Laboratory where Professor Lindemann held the chair. Both
Lindemann (later Lord Cherwell) and Tizard were well aware of his aptitude
for Intelligence work, and Woodward-Nutt, who had replaced Rowe as
secretary of the Tizard Committee, had worked with Jones at the Air Defence
Experimental Department at Farnborough and knew him well. Woodward-
Nutt had suggested to Tizard that Jones should be brought back to the Air
Ministry as 'a scientist with a special interest in German weapons' and Tizard
strongly supported the proposal. Jones was attached to the Air Intelligence
branch of the Air Ministry, then headed by Wing Commander F.W.
Winterbotham, and known as AI i(c), the air component of MI6, the Secret
Intelligence Service.

[2] Jones. Letter to the author.

It seems incredible that at this time Britain had no extensive organisation within its Intelligence Service for securing information about German scientific progress, and even more remarkable that Jones's position was that of a 'one-man enquiry into why so little scientific and technical information was being obtained by our Intelligence Services, and to recommend ways in which the arrangements could be improved.' This lack of forethought on the part of Whitehall and the Service Ministries prompted Jones to investigate the background, and ten weeks after taking up his appointment he drew up a report entitled *A Scientific Intelligence Service* which, among other observations, remarked, '...enquiries have shown that there has been no systematic observation of evidence indicating German RDF (radar) transmissions.'

'I drew attention,' recalls Jones in *Most Secret War*, 'to an important weakness in our Intelligence cover in that there was no organisation to listen to German transmissions that might be connected with radar or radio navigation.'

Despite this, Whitehall's curious reluctance to take the matter seriously was evidenced a few weeks later when, in December 1939, the *Admiral Graf Spee* was scuttled off the River Plate. One of the British radar team, L.H. Bainbridge-Bell, inspected the structure mounted on the optical range-finder and concluded that it was a radar antenna and that the wavelength was about 80 cm, but his report was shelved for 18 months, during which time Whitehall still continued to debate whether the Germans actually had radar.

It was not until 1940 when monitoring of German radio-telephony traffic between their aircraft and ground control revealed that a German fighter had intercepted a British bomber through 'the excellent *Freya-Meldung*' (Freya Reporting) and as this term seemed to be connected with a form of air defence, Jones wondered whether anything in the legend of the goddess Freya would give a clue. A few days later he issued a report called *The Edda Revived*:

Actually the Decknammen Department of the Luftwaffe could hardly have chosen a more fruitful goddess, but few of her attributes have any possible relation with the present problem. She did, however, have as her most prized possession a necklace, Brisinga-men, to obtain which she not merely sacrificed, but massacred her honour. The necklace is important because it was guarded by Heimdall, the watchman of the gods, who could see a hundred miles by day and night. There is a possible association of ideas with a coastal chain and a detecting system with a range of a hundred miles … it is unwise to lay too much stress on this evidence, but these are the only facts concerning Freya which seem to have any relation to our previous knowledge. Actually Heimdall himself would have been the best choice for a code-name for RDF, but perhaps he would have been too obvious.

It is difficult to escape the conclusion, therefore, that the *Freya-Gerät* is a form of portable RDF.

The report concluded with the observation that *Freya* stations were believed to have been installed near Cherbourg and Brest, and it was later learned that the Cherbourg installation had located the destroyer *Delight* at a range of 60 miles and that the Luftwaffe had sunk her. It appeared this particular radar was situated near the village of Auderville, but up to now the Photographic Reconnaissance Unit (PRU) had not located it. This suggested the apparatus was much smaller than the British Chain Home installations.

The first success came in January 1941 when the Photographic Reconnaissance Unit took a pair of stereo pictures of two small circles in a field. Claude Wavell, Jones's liaison officer in the Photographic Interpretation Unit, thought they might be nothing more than cattle troughs or 'cow-bins' as he called them, although he thought they were odd enough to draw to Jones's attention:

> …they were near a village and I asked him its name. 'Auderville' he replied, and a bell rang loudly in my mind … could these 20 foot circles be the Freya for which we had been so fruitlessly searching?

Jones and his assistant Dr Charles Frank examined them in turn, and it was Frank who noticed that the shadows were of different widths in successive photographs, and as nine seconds had elapsed between each photo it was obvious that the difference was caused by something rotating. The difference, in fact, was only about a tenth of a millimetre on the picture but it was positive. Jones at once called for a low-level oblique photograph from the PRU, and on 22 February Flying Officer W.K. Manifould returned with two excellent photographs with 'the two circles beautifully centred'. There was no doubt that these were radar installations, and Wavell agreed with it. (These were later forms of rotating *Freyas*.)

During this period Air Marshal Joubert had been appointed Adviser for Combined Operations and had convened a meeting for 24 February to 'discuss the existence of German radar'. The timing of Manifould's sortie was, therefore, most opportune, but the photos were not the only evidence Jones took to the meeting. Despite his warning in 1939 that no proper monitoring service existed for German radar transmissions, little had been done about it and the gap had once again to be filled by individual enterprise. This was undertaken by Derek Garrard of the Telecommunications Research Establishment, who had been detached from that organisation to become an assistant to Jones, but who was not content to kick his heels in an office until his security clearance was obtained.

> Impatient at having so little to do in my Air Ministry office, Garrard acquired a suitable radio receiver and took it in his own car down to the south coast to see if he could find the missing Freya transmissions since the official listening service had failed. In the course of a few highly profitable days, which included his getting arrested as a Fifth Columnist for his unauthorised activity in a Defended Area, he succeeded in hearing the *Freya* transmissions on frequencies of about 120 megacycles a second, or 2.5 metres wavelength, and even in getting rough bearings on where they came from. Some of his bearings in fact intersected near the very equipment we had now photographed north-west of Cherbourg. It was a most valuable individual effort, and Garrard returned with his results on the very morning of Joubert's meeting on 24 February.
>
> So when the meeting started, I let it run on for a little to let the doubters say that they did not believe that the Germans had any radar, and then I produced both the photographs and Garrard's bearings. Joubert looked hard at me and said, 'How long have you had this evidence, Jones?' He obviously suspected that I had kept it up my sleeve just to make fools of the doubters, perhaps for weeks. I pointed to the date inscribed on the sortie showing that it had been taken only two days ago. That was the end of disbelief in German radar.

The British would doubtless have been astonished to learn that this radar had its origins in experiments which had taken place more than ten years earlier, and apart from the Oslo Report, it is a tribute to the German Security Service that it remained a secret for so long. But in 1941 it was clear to the British that the Germans had at least three forms of radar: one on around 80 cm for naval purposes, the *Freya* on 125 MHz, and the Oslo

Report spoke of another on 50 cm. But what was it? And if it came to that, where was it?

By now the cryptographers at Bletchley Park had succeeded in breaking the German *Enigma* cipher[1], and the first clue to Jones was a signal saying that a *Freya* was being sent to Rumania for coastal surveillance, and that a pair of *Würzburgs* were on their way to Bulgaria for the same purpose. Jones calculated that these were probably the minimum number of equipments that could sweep the Black Sea coasts of both countries, say 260 km for Rumania and 150 km for Bulgaria. In the latter case each *Würzburg* would cover about 75 km of coastline, which was possible if the radar had an all-round range of 37.5 km, and the *Freya* would have a range of some 92.5 km to sweep the Rumanian coast.

From Garrard's findings he knew the *Freya* had a prf of 1,000 Hz and its range must therefore be about 150 km, which seemed about right for a minimum of 92.5 km if the Rumanian evidence could be believed. Examined in this light, if the *Würzburg* had a range of about 40 km it should have a prf of around 3,750 Hz and, if the Oslo Report was right, be operating on 50 cm.

> With these figures in mind, we searched and found the transmissions: their wavelengths were about 53 centimetres, and the pulse repetition rate was 3750. The first transmissions that we detected came from the Channel coast, and the next obvious step was to locate a site accurately enough for photographs to be taken. For the moment, though, this was impossible – it had been difficult enough to find the first *Freya* on a photograph, and *Würzburg* was certainly smaller.

As it turned out, the *Würzburg* was eventually photographed in much the same way as the *Freya*, but the story belongs to another chapter.

The question is often asked: were the Germans aware of British radar development? The short answer is that they suspected it was going ahead. From a statistical viewpoint alone it would be illogical to imagine Britain without some form of radar system

---

[1] Bletchley Park, or 'Station X' as it was known, was the evacuation headquarters of MI6 and also housed the Government Code and Cipher School (GCCS), then headed by Commander Alexander Denniston. The breaking of the German Enigma cipher was a brilliant achievement by a team of dedicated cryptographers who worked almost non-stop to bring this about.

at a time when most world powers, or at least the scientists among them, knew the principle. The Germans knew, for instance, that the French had a system called *Détection Electro-Magnétique* (DEM) and that it was practically useless, and all the technical world had heard of the pulse system designed for the liner *Normandie* for detecting icebergs.

From a strategic viewpoint also it seemed most likely that Britain would need to have a form of early warning. The relative strengths of both air forces were known, and German military thinking insisted that the diminutive Royal Air Force must depend on something else besides determination and obsolete sound locators, this thought being principally held by Generals Milch and Udet who visited RAF units in 1937, and caused several wine glasses to fall to the Mess floor by asking, 'Now how are you chaps getting on with your radar? We know you've got it!'[1]

Clearly, the 350 foot towers of the British *Chain Home* system could not be hidden from the Heinkel He111s of Lufthansa, which ostensibly carrying out weather reporting were really engaged on photo reconnaissance, so a disinformation exercise was instituted to suggest they were radio ground control stations. Martini was reluctant to believe this and carried out his own radio monitoring programme by flying up and down the east coast of Britain in the *Graf Zeppelin*, its gondola packed with radio equipment. According to some reports all he received for his trouble was a lot of static, and while this is probably true he did not fail to detect the 12 metre transmissions from the stations he passed,[2] all of which, of course, were enjoying this large-scale location exercise. And while he found it hard to believe the British were using the 12

[1] In October 1937 Generals Milch, Udet and Stumpf inspected RAF Fighter Command at Hornchurch by invitation. Milch claimed that more than one glass fell to the floor when he said, 'Now gentlemen, let us all be frank. How are you getting on with your experiments in the detection by radio of aircraft off your shores? We've known for some time that you are developing a system of radiolocation. So are we, and we think we are a jump ahead of you.'

[2] Some commentators have observed that Martini could have been misled as to the location of the Chain Home signals, arguing that as he was over the North Sea at the time, he could have been deceived by signals from the continent on the same frequency. This will not hold water for a number of reasons. First, Martini was head of Luftwaffe Signals and knew his job, second, direction-finding with sense antennas was a German speciality, and third, on one occasion the airship was actually nine miles inland over England! In any event Martini told Runge of his suspicions and complained that no one would take him seriously. (Runge to author)

metre band for radar when the Germans had been using centimetres for years, he found it harder to believe that these stations could be used for ground control purposes in the accepted sense. His suspicions, although well founded, came too late for inclusion in General Schmid's *Studie Blau*, a textbook for the Luftwaffe on British defences, and in any case the war broke out shortly afterwards and left the Luftwaffe in no doubt as to the existence and potency of British radar.

CHAPTER THREE

Runge's Memoirs and the Expanding Programme

The contribution of Telefunken (now AEG) the largest and most influential company in the realm of electronics, is all the more unique in view of the part played by one of its most outstanding figures, the late Professor Dr Wilhelm T. Runge, for many years Head of Development, and the guiding force behind the emergence of many well-known radar systems. His personal account of those early days, as given to the author, throws light on a number of aspects of the German radar programme hitherto unpublished.

'How did we arrive at radar? I know we began experiments with the development of new valves, small glass-enveloped triodes known as 'Acorn' valves. And I don't remember whether this technology of the American 'Acorn' valve was borrowed from them or came from our own ideas – I am inclined to believe the latter, because at that time the Americans were much slower than we were in producing centimetric wavelengths. These valves oscillated on 50 centimetres and delivered about one tenth of a watt, and these were the only valves available to me. I set myself up in an empty room at number 10 Templehofufer, in Berlin, as a one-man laboratory to experiment with centimetric waves, and as I found contact detectors to be unreliable for reception I used small hot-cathode diodes with very small electrode spacing, and detected directional patterns, measured the resonant lengths of dipoles, and the action of reflectors, walls, standing waves and so on.

'Later on, this work was continued by a man called Roosenstein, but his heart was not really in the work and he took up other interests. Then a technician called Rosenow began to show some interest, but unfortunately he died shortly after he had begun. Some modest long-term research was carried out between us and the Army Reservists in 1932, mainly communication on these frequencies over the small distance between number 9 Templehofufer and number 12 Halleschesufer – all part of the Telefunken complex of course.

'Quite independently of us, another Telefunken Group was also working in the centimetric field. This was led by Dr Ilberg in co-operation with another group under Dr Alexander Meissner at our Research Institute Physics Laboratory, where they worked with Barkhausen-Kurz valves. These had tungsten cathodes, but as they were strongly over-heated they had a correspondingly short life. Compared to my diodes they were very sensitive, but unreliable as detectors.

'The real trouble started in 1933 when Hitler came to power. That man caused considerable interference with the running of the firm. We had a man in the firm called Captain Scharlau, who was the adviser to our Export Sales Group. It turned out that he was a Party member, one of the old chums in fact, and one of the first jobs he was ordered to do by that lot was to clean the firm of what they called "opposing elements", in other words the Jews. Our Director, Emil Mayer, was the first to go, and with him of course most of the company top brass. Mayer was replaced by a man called Schwab who had been a U-boat commander amongst other things, but he had very little idea of how to run a large company and he, too, was eventually replaced by Dr Rukop.

'Scharlau demanded that the company leadership, which up to then had always catered for customer requirements, should now be re-orientated. Telefunken must now look forward and carry out more research. They gave me an interim grant of 20,000 marks for early development (such as it was) of centimetric systems, and ordered Dr Ilberg's Group to come under my jurisdiction. We made the best of a bad bargain, and at least space was freely made and we could think of other things – the building of a new workshop, for instance. But to get back to the subject …

'The chief characteristic of centimetric waves was their directive qualities, and we proved these propagation features by numerous tests out in the country. We used directional antennas based on the *Tannenbaum* pattern with sheet metal reflectors, and superhet receivers were now employed, as opposed to the TRF and superregenerative receivers we had tried earlier. The transmitter of course was a simple self-excited affair, and modulated even more simply by the anode voltage (amplitude modulation – or so we liked to believe) but Dr von Radinger, one of our colleagues, always maintained that the transmitter should employ frequency modulation, as should of course the receivers. I was against the idea. But in spite of my objections von Radinger went ahead and built a frequency demodulator after the IF stages of the receiver. I must admit that the test results were decisive. The ignition interference from our cars, in which we had driven to the country, played havoc with the AM signals, but with FM the reception was very good, quite a low noise-level in fact. I mentally tipped my hat to von Radinger.

'We had set ourselves two aims for the exercise: radio ranging and navigation. And we obtained a great deal of experience about ranges. We built up a reversal switch, so that by alternately switching a pair of antennas to a pre-determined angle, the transmitter would generate an equi-signal path. Of course, when Scharlau heard about this he immediately thought about a fog-warning system in place of lights. In a way this idea was to prove useful because for the kind of tests we were thinking about we were given a research station at Kiel, a transmitter installation in Friedrichsort, and a control station in Laboe on the other side of the harbour.

'It was there, during our tests, that we first observed the effects of reflections from naval ships – as a matter of fact the transmitter and receiver were far removed from each other, but these ships cruised across the beams almost continuously, or an aircraft flew overhead, and these reflections were more of a nuisance than anything else. I did not give much attention to this phenomenon for some time, although an idea was always in the back of my mind that we could put these reflections to another use.

'But before I come on to that, I ought to say something about the development of our directional radio. During our experiments we gained a great deal of experience with our self-oscillating transmitters, superhets, frequency modulation and so on. And we also had a lot of success with quadratic directional antennas with 1 metre length sides, so much so that during the Army manoeuvres of 1936 they asked us for twenty medium-size radio-telephony link stations. We designed these so that the transmitter and the receiver mixing stage were supported along with the antenna on the top of telescopic masts, and the modulation and power cables were led down the mast to the power supply unit and the receiver IF stages. We called these "Olympia Masts", simply because the 1936 Olympic games were held in Berlin, and the name "Olympia" was a symbol of the times. Opel, for instance, had brought out a new car called the Opel Olympia.[1]

'These installations were very successful. We could bridge line-of-sight distances of up to 70 km quite easily, and in some cases well up to 100 km. In fact, General Fellgiebel[2] of the Army High Command had a conversation with me and expressed his praise for the technique, remarking how small the cost would be for cable and other material, and how simple such a stretch of communication links would be to build and, if necessary, guard. The upshot of this conversation was that plans were put in motion for a large and sophisticated communications link to cover the whole country, and later on, others as well. As a matter of fact, it turned out that the Luftwaffe took charge of the business and drew up plans for three types of equipment: a small one called *K* and a medium size one called *M* for relay stages, together with one known as *R* which was to carry nine radio-telephone channels. *M* and *R* we code-named *Michael* and *Rudolf* respectively, and we had the exclusive contract for these. *K*, for some reason I can't remember, went to Lorenz. *Rudolf* was never completely finished during the war, and therefore played no important part in it, and as for *K* I never knew much about it.

'*Michael* was ready by 1938, but we had many developmental problems still to overcome. For example, they wanted the equipment at the top of the mast to be placed under the ground, and this meant that we had to develop special centimetric coaxial cable in our cable factory, and for the frequency modulation of the transmitters this new cable had, of course, to match the antenna perfectly. This involved not only a great deal of measurement techniques, but also a host of other details that had our technicians running in all directions. It was a very busy and demanding time. Our people were extremely over-worked, and even Father Mass, our Chaplain – oh yes, they let us have some spiritual consolation, I don't know why – was affected by it. I came into my office one morning and found a note on the desk: "Dear Doctor, please excuse my

[1] The version often reported in other works that Telefunken had been asked to provide a radio link between the Olympic stadium and the main broadcasting station is incorrect. Runge assured me that his own account is authentic. *Author*.

[2] Fellgiebel was amongst those who attempted to assassinate Hitler and was later executed.

absence from the discussion this morning, but I've got a wedding to conduct. I'll be back at twelve."

'In the event, we tackled all the problems and got on top of them, and from 1938 to the end of the war *Michael* was delivered in large numbers. Its noise-suppression was so good that all sectors could be consecutively connected, and this enabled a network to be built that covered the whole of occupied Europe up to the Krim, and from Narvik right through to Crete – a total distance of 70,000 kilometres. But our efforts to open up the 20 cm band for radio-telephony techniques were always plagued by the problem of getting transmitting valves of suffecent power. Triodes of the power we would have liked just were not obtainable, and the "split magnetrons" we managed to get from our valve department were not stable enough. But Dr Illberg's Group came up with some research types which worked quite well on 5 centimetres, and in fact, we managed to build a system which gave us a direct radio link from the Brocken (the highest peak in the Hartz mountains) to Berlin. In fact, I think your Intelligence people got wind of our experiments on the Brocken before the war, although I don't think they knew exactly what we were doing.[1]

'But of course the shorter the wavelength so our receiver sensitivity was reduced, especially as our receivers used hot-cathode diodes in the mixer stage. In fact, for 5 centimetres we often used a simple crystal detector in place of the frequency changer, but for all practical purposes this was not good enough. In any case we had to break off our work in this field in the autumn of 1942 to concentrate on developments for the armed forces, and we were by then heavily overburdened by their demands. By then of course, your English laboratories had made progress in the design and manufacture of synthetic

[1] The British knew that the Germans were undertaking VHF radio developments on the Brocken. The information came to Jones in 1938, shortly before he took up his post at the Admiralty Research Laboratory, when he was for a time attached to Group Captain H. Leedham, the Assistant Director of Instrument Research and Development at the Air Ministry. One of his tasks was to examine the reports from Air Intelligence, and the activity on the Brocken was mentioned. Later, Jones learned from Dr Charles Frank, who was holidaying in Germany, of the existence of an array of posts 'rather like Belisha beacons with wooden pear-shaped objects at the top'. Later, a German refugee said that vehicles were often stopped by guards because the receivers could be easily jammed by ignition interference, this period presumably being before von Radinger's change to FM. (The Brocken, according to legend, was also the home of the goddess Freya).

semi-conductor diodes. These were things that had never come to my mind, mainly because I had learnt only a little physics, and I was too involved with trying to find a breakthrough into high-vacuum valves for radio techniques. I think too, that we had also concentrated a great deal on measuring techniques for receiver sensitivity on centimetric wavelengths, and we certainly led the field in this race.

'But to return to your question about these reflected signals which were always cropping up during our tests at Kiel.

'In the summer of 1935 I was at our research establishment at Gross Ziethen when I hit on the idea of seeing just what these reflected waves might do. I took one of our 1 metre square antennas and laid it flat on the ground, and coupled it up to one of these 0.1 watt tone-modulated transmitters I described earlier on. Next to it I arranged a similar antenna which was connected to a simple receiver with a diode detector, followed by an audio frequency amplifier which had a valve voltmeter, or S-meter in its circuit.

'As soon as I had switched everything on, I happened to notice one of Telefunken's own Junkers Ju52s at 5000 metres (16,500 feet) on her outward flight on some business or other, and as it drew closer to the directional beam from the transmitter I noticed the S-meter begin to flutter, just small movements at first, then, as the aircraft flew overhead, the needle went right over and began to move slowly between zero and full-scale deflection. To tell the truth I was immediately excited. Such a simple set-up! 5,000 metres range and the effect on the receiver!

'I couldn't contain myself, I cried out, "With this equipment you could slaughter an ox!" I ran hot-foot into Rukop's office and told him what I had discovered, but he didn't turn a hair. He didn't show the slightest interest. As far as he was concerned I might have been remarking on the weather.

'I went back to my own office and thought about it, and as I did so, I remembered that about a year earlier I had had an unsolicited and unexpected visit from Kühnhold, the Technical Head of the Navy's Communication Research Establishment at Kiel. He had wanted me to take on his own reflecting-wave work, but I couldn't agree to it because it seemed a bit far-fetched to me. Evidently Kühnhold took my refusal to be the official attitude of the company, and he went away to form the Gema Company which subsequently carried out the development of *Freya* for the Navy.

'I thought about my discovery for some time, and then I

came to a decision. If Rukop wasn't interested, *I* was. I summed up the situation very carefully and decided to go ahead with further experiments on my own initiative. I even decided to use "black funds", that is, money really intended for other work, on the project. I let Dr Muth in on the secret, and placed him in charge of the circuitry development. It was soon clear to us that pulse transmission had to be used, and Muth pushed our small valves to pulse-peaks of 15 watts. Two forms of receiver were considered, the "A" circuit, where the receiver remained on the whole time and was suppressed only during the transmitted pulses, and the "B" circuit, where the receiver was suppressed and only activated by a pulse, the time interval of the transmitted pulse being adjusted by phase-shifting. The cathode-ray tubes we used for the "A" system were rather primitive at that time, but they gave a fairly good general view, and we were very pleased with them when we used them with the "B" system for range-measurements. We had very suitable results then.

'One of my earliest recollections is of the equipment we took into the country for testing. The first returned echo was about two microseconds away from the transmitted pulse, and seemed to come from a wire fence about 300 metres away. I thought, "That's impossible! The trace is too slow. Two whole microseconds up to that fence and back ...?" Microseconds were quite an advanced thing for us in those days ...

'On two occasions in the summer of 1936 we put our gear in a truck and made some tests over the Baltic. We installed the equipment on a steep bank near Neustein, a town to the east of Laboe, and observed our ranges against the shipping. These, in fact, were quite poor because 15 watts of power was just not good enough. Then I had an idea. I mounted a dipole at the focal point of a parabolic reflector in such a way that the dipole could be rotated. We even found a nickname for this device: a *Quirl*. This generated a cone-shaped beam with which we could now make reasonable measurements of the range. From this arrangement we designed a new equipment which we code-named *Darmstadt*, and with this we could detect an aircraft at about 5 kilometres. Not a very useful distance, I admit, but our transmitters just couldn't deliver a higher power. I'm not sure how we chose the code-names for our equipment, but I think someone looked at a map and selected town names, such as Darmstadt, Mannheim, Würzburg, Mainz and so on just for convenience. *Lichtenstein* was different. The set had to be small enough to fit into an aircraft, and I think we chose the name from the Lichtenstein Schloss near Bad Wurtemburg.

'While we were carrying out our experiments with *Darmstadt* Muth became very ill and his place was taken by one of his colleagues called Stepp. We managed to increase the power quite considerably, and we constructed a new paraboloid of about 3 metres diameter made out of wire mesh on a wooden frame. This was mounted on gimbals with a wooden axle at the rear for height and bearing adjustments. In fact, this new system was so reliable that in the summer of 1938 I demonstrated it to General Udet, the Quartermaster General of the Luftwaffe. He was, of course, an old aviator of the First World War, and I rather think he still lived in those days. At any rate, when I explained that it could be used to cover a 50 km area, and that in spite of fog, or at night, it would locate an aircraft easily within that range, his reaction was astonishing. "Good God! If you introduce that thing you'll take all the fun out of flying!" I was so annoyed that I just span round on my heel and left him. Obviously I had said the wrong thing. Of course, the Flak was not there to protect the Luftwaffe, and in any case it came under the control of the Army in those days, so perhaps his reaction was understandable if not excusable.

'As I mentioned, Kühnhold had gone ahead and founded his Gema Company. And by this time I think his *Freya* had a range of about 100 kilometres against aircraft. But it never seemed to occur to him that there were other people besides himself who were concerned with radar techniques.

'I had given a lecture at the Lilienthal Institut about the possibility of using the pulse-timing of radio pulses on centimetres – an open lecture, mind you, – and there was an attempt to charge me with violating matters of national security!

'And do you know, at the beginning of 1939 he complained to our directors up about our "unauthorised reflecting-wave work" as he called it. He thought we could never have any success with it because we wouldn't be able to develop enough power on 50 centimetres. Now Rukop had always had ambitions to develop better valves, and he was stung into action. He jumped to his feet and glared across the table. "In six weeks we will produce a 10 kilowatt valve for 600 MHz!"

'And he did! In fact, in just under six weeks we had the first model of the LS 180 pulse triode. And as the range increased with the fourth root of the power we attained 40 kilometres quite easily. Of course, this was no great distance, but for the Flak it would be ample. We began at once to develop the transmitter circuitry for these new valves, and, as you might

Above Christian Hülsmeyer at age 23
(*Annelise Hecker-Hülsmeyer*)

Above right Christian Hülsmeyer at 74
years of age (*Annelise
Hecker-Hülsmeyer*)

Right Tablet on Hülsmeyer's home
(*Annelise Hecker-Hülsmeyer*)

IN·DIESEM·HAUSE·LEBTE·VO
1930·BIS·ZU·SEINEM·TODE·19
DER·UR·RADAR·ERFINDER
ING. CHR. HÜLSMEYE
GEB. 25.12.1881·IN·EYDELSTEL
DAS·HÜLSMEYER·PATENT·WA
DAS·ALLERERSTE
RADAR·PATENT·DER·WELT
DRP·165546 v. 30.4.1904

DIESE·TAFEL·ENTSTAND·ANLÄSSLICH·DER·W
70·JAHREN (1904) AN·DER·RHEINBRÜCKE
KÖLN·UND·AUF·DEM·INTERN·SCHIFFAHR
KONGRESS·IN·ROTTERDAM·ERFOLGE
VORGEFÜHRTEN·PRAKTISCHEN·VERSUC

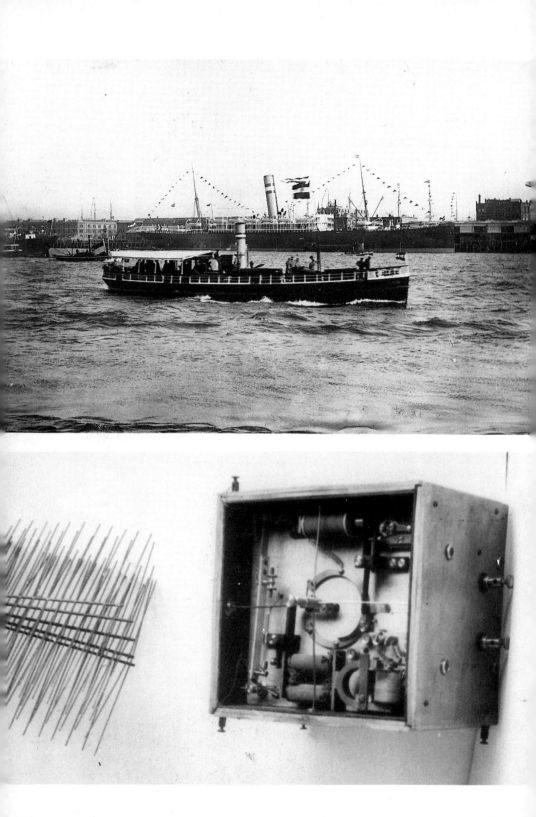

Left The tender
Columbus which
carried Hülsmeyer's
demonstration
equipment in 1904
(*Archivdienst
Rotterdam*)

Below left Antenna
director elements and
receiver from
Hülsmeyer's early radar
circa 1904 (*Fritz
Trenkle*)

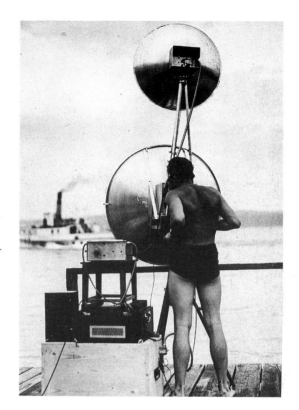

Above right Reflecting
wave research with
continuous-wave radar
against a steamer on
Lake Ammer in 1937.
10 cm wavelength with
speed measurement by
Doppler Effect (*Fritz
Trenkle*)

Right The first Flak
radar, the *FMG (Flak)
38 L Kurfürst*, mounted
on an 88 mm Flak gun
(*Fritz Trenkle*)

Left The First *Freya* erected on the island of Wangerooge (*Fritz Trenkle*)

Below One of the first series of the *FMG (Flum) 39 G (fB) Freya* (*Fritz Trenkle*)

expect, the high pulsing at 10 kilowatts immediately posed fresh problems, but with the help of Dr Pederanzi and Stepp these were soon ironed out. What we really wanted was a good production line, but where were the customers to come from? The Navy was annoyed with us, and in any case had their Freya and Seetakt models, the latter by the way operating originally on about 50 centimetres despite Kühnhold's statements. The Army were uninterested because they were already trying out another system, I think it must have been the *Kurfürst* from Lorenz, but I'm not sure, and the Luftwaffe had no interest in air defence techniques. We were rather stumped.

'To give you some idea of the state of chaos then prevailing in the Services, the Luftwaffe in particular never seemed to know what they wanted. One department said one thing, and this was usually countermanded by another, but by 1939 things were beginning to sort themselves out, and in that year we received a firm order for an early-warning system which had to be much smaller than Kühnhold's *Freya*, and, more importantly, extremely mobile. To this end we designed an equipment with a 3 metre diameter parabolic reflector and a fixed dipole, an operating bench which revolved with the equipment, and with handles to orientate it for height and bearing. For transportation we made the reflector so that it would fold in half, and the entire apparatus was mounted on four wheels. Someone stuck a pin in the map and we called it the *Würzburg* A.

'This had to be sent to Rechlin for testing (which it passed with flying colours) and of course I had to go down there from time to time on official business. One evening I had my first real scare of the war. One of our chief aircraft designers, a man named Müller, offered to fly me back to Berlin in a Storch, but before we could leave they found a slight fault with the plane which had to be put right. This of course made our take-off a little late. But it was a wonderful evening: the sun was low in a crimson sky as we approached Berlin. Actually we were heading for a small airfield near Lake Diepen to the south of the city, but we had to make a wide arc because our own aircraft were forbidden to fly over it. Now a flight in a Storch is very different from one in a passenger aircraft. You sit in a tiny cabin and fly slowly, barely 400 feet high, but from where you can see everything on the ground.

'The twilight began to descend. And this was a bit unnerving because we were not equipped for night flying and in any case night flying for us was prohibited. Furthermore, the airfield we were heading for had no beacon lights, it was wartime after all. I could still see reasonably well. I recognised the southern ring of the autobahn along which we were flying, until, suddenly, Müller banked to the left and followed the railway. I got disorientated and was worried for a moment, until I thought, "Oh well, Müller knows where we are. We won't miss the airfield."

'At that moment Müller turned to me and yelled, "Where *is* Lake Diepen for God's sake?"

'Now I had tried to remember the plan of the railway but Müller's shout put me off. I had a vague feeling we had come a bit too much to the right, and I lifted my hand to scratch my jaw in thought. Müller took this to mean that we should go left, and at once put the Storch into a steep left curve – much to my misery because now I had no idea where we were – but he had already spotted the airfield in spite of the gathering gloom, and calmly proceeded to fly over Berlin with no form of identification and without lights. I confidently expected to be shot out of the sky at any moment, but for some reason the Flak didn't open fire and we finally touched down in one piece. I raced from the plane and hurled myself into my car with infinite relief ...

'In the summer of 1940 the Television Development Group under Dr Urtel came to join us, and this was a very valuable reinforcement. Urtel got busy straight away by forming a team for developing centimetric measuring techniques, one of the team, a Dr Kettel, turned out to be an excellent researcher into pulse problems, circuitry, precise pulse-time measurements and so on. And of course, these television people understood much more about cathode-ray tubes than we did.

'In August the RAF began their bombing raids on Berlin, and we had to produce a more accurate version of the *Würzburg* "A", in fact, it was more of a reconstruction, and for this we used the *Quirl* and a new plotting circuit with better cathode-ray tubes, a project, incidentally, in which Urtel's people were especially successful. And it was this that gave me my second scare of the war. The first model of our new design was installed in a Flak battery near Osdorf, just south of Berlin, and when I received warning that a raid was imminent one evening, I drove down there to see how it performed. It located a target at about 35 kilometres and began to deliver its data to the battery, whose guns swung round at once. The battery let the target come on for about 10 kilometres then opened fire, and just after that first shot the young *Leutnant* in charge yelled something to me. I turned round and glanced at the equipment, and a shiver of apprehension ran down my back. The screens were blank and the whole apparatus had gone cold. What the hell was wrong with it? It was perfect when it was delivered to the battery ... I made a quick examination and to my relief found that a plug had become disconnected due to the vibration from the shot. Someone had forgotten to tighten the locking ring.

'As it happened, I had very little to do with subsequent developments of the *Würzburg* series, except at administrative level, because my various teams working on them were so well organised that they could carry on my work without my breathing down their backs. The *Würzburg A*, for example, was now well under way with a large staff of people headed by Leo Brandt, and it was in fact Brandt who developed the *Würzburg Riese* with its 7 metre diameter parabolic reflector. But the work on the *Würzburg* series was in any case seriously hampered in 1943 because we had to develop methods of overcoming the British dropping of *Window*. You used this for the first time during the heavy raids on Hamburg, and believe me, this caused serious problems for our defences.

'The irony of the situation was that we already knew about *Window*. We called it *Düppel*. And in fact it was Dr Roosenstein who had developed it in early 1942 and tested it over the Baltic[1], but I can tell you it scared the pants off Göring. "If the British ever get to know about this," he said, "we'll be in serious trouble." So any mention of *Düppel* was prohibited under pain of heavy penalties, but I think your people got to hear about it anyway.[2]

'*Lichtenstein*? Well now, I'll tell you the story from the beginning. A young relative of mine was a pilot in a dive bomber squadron, and on one occasion they attacked the enemy from a considerable height and, owing to a low cloud base, nearly went into the ground. Now earlier on, in 1939 in fact, Muth had co-operated with me in the design of a small reflecting-wave equipment for measuring an aircraft's height, an altimeter in fact, but with circuitry so designed that, in conjunction with a servo-system, the aircraft would automa-

---

[1] The first trials were carried out on the Düppel Estate near Berlin, hence the name.

[2] They had. In October 1942 Jones received a report from a Danish agent who had overheard two Luftwaffe women personnel talking about it in a railway train.

tically pull out of a dive at a certain minimum height. In 1940 we actually brought out a research model, but the thing was far too big to go into an aircraft, so we put it on a shelf in the laboratory and forgot about it.

'A few weeks later Martini, the Head of Luftwaffe Signals, came to ask me if we could build a small airborne radar which the night-fighters in Holland could use for finding enemy bombers. I sat and thought about it for a while, and suddenly remembered this research model. I thought it could be put to use here. It would of course need a sensitive receiver with a cathode-ray tube and, above all, a new type of directional antenna. Obviously, even a 1 metre diameter paraboloid with a *Quirl* would cause far too much air resistance. Well, to cut a long story short, we re-designed the original equipment and managed to make it much smaller – it was only assembly line work really – and we gave it an air test in August. Its range was only about 4 kilometres, and you could only track one aircraft at a time, and even then it had to be a steadily-flown target. A nightfighter squadron in Holland sent us a Me110 in which we installed the equipment – and then I heard nothing more about it. I suppose it must have been about six months later when I saw Martini again, and I asked him about the tests as I had had no news. He told me a story that would have had me hugging my sides if it wasn't so pathetic. It turned out that the aircraft and its equipment still stood unused in a hangar, and this was the reason:

'This particular squadron was made up of officers mainly from the highest ranks of German society – all honourable, noble young gentlemen brought up in the traditions of Richthofen, Boelcke and Immelmann etc., and they considered this new-fangled technical stuff to be unsportsmanlike in the highest degree. Now it happened that one of them came from a working-class background, and they felt his presence distinctly embarrassing. The chap himself felt very much a fish out of water. He had had only three brushes with the enemy, but had only managed to shoot one of them down, and had been shot down a couple of times himself for his pains. Fed up with this state of affairs, he took the aircraft out of its hangar and flew it down to Berlin and asked us to give him some training in the use of the radar. We were only too pleased to help, and when he felt confident about it, he flew back to his squadron. Then we heard nothing more about him.

'Nothing more, that is, until another six months had passed, and I was once more chatting to Martini. I happened to ask if he had heard anything about this youngster, and he told me the sequel.

'Apparently, during his first action with the radar he found a target, but was so nervous that he overshot his position and had to break away. He found it again, but he was so full of nerves that he ruined his approach several times. He then decided to take a grip of himself and calm down, with the result that he eventually shot his target down. Later that night he shot another two down. And another two on the following night. Then the commanding officer grounded him, because at the rate he was going he would have been the first to receive an Iron Cross, First Class. And to be awarded that distinction for such unsportsmanlike methods would never do ...

'Anyway, we were still busy with the routine development of this equipment, but even after several models were produced, and a modest number delivered, it never achieved anything of significance until the daylight bombing raids began. And then we had the shock of our lives.

'At the beginning of 1943 a British aircraft was shot down near Rotterdam, and in it we found an entirely new type of ground-search radar which worked on 9 centimetres. Now up to then we knew very little about British radar technology, except that we thought it was rather primitive, but now we stood looking at an extremely superior system which employed a cavity magnetron, and known to your people as H₂S/ASV. Even Göring was impressed. He grumbled about us lagging behind you in the radar race and gave us a hell of a dressing down. Well, after he had cooled off we made a searching examination of this new equipment, and I'm bound to say that we were full of admiration for the people who had designed and built it. It was a godsend to us, and why you allowed it to fall into our hands I'll never know. It would have been much safer to let it be used only as ASV radar, but I suppose your strategists thought otherwise. In the event, we copied it and from this we designed our own similar system which we called *Berlin*.

'In a way I was annoyed about it because our own 5 centimetre research was begun before the war, but we had to break it off in 1942 because of other more urgent developments, even though I had demonstrated the possibilities of this centimetric idea to the three Services. Now of course they came rushing back to me to get something done quickly on these lines, but I had already given orders for the research into what we later called the *Berlin* system, and this called for the design and production of thousands of synthetic diodes. Even then, these had to be used in large numbers for our radar-warning device Naxos, although I wasn't involved very much in that.

'The only thing I had to do in this connection was to go to France at the request of the Navy, to find out how your people were able to detect our U-boats so easily in the Bay of Biscay. Up to then you hadn't used your centimetric system, but you had a 1.25 metre search radar in your aircraft, and the radiation from these sets was constantly being picked up on the U-boats' warning receivers. Actually, these receivers were the responsibility of the Naval Communications Research Establishment and had been developed by the French firm Metox. I had the suspicion that these might not be sufficiently screened, and could be picking up the U-boats' own broader radio beacon signals, so I went to Bordeaux where there was a Reconnaissance Squadron who had on their station a transmitter working on the Metox frequency. It was soon clear that its transmissions could be heard at 80 kilometres, and the report of this effect on the U-boats' receivers was immediately suppressed, but by then it was too late.'

*

As Runge's account, by its very nature, does not follow a strict chronological order of radar development, it should be pointed out that the *Darmstadt* experimental model was the forerunner of a series of Flak radars, including the *Mainz* and *Mannheim* and, of course, the *Würzburg A* as mentioned. All these worked in what was called simultaneous operation, that is, the same antenna was used for transmitting and receiving by using special switching so that much the same performance was obtained with what virtually amounted to half the antenna area.

A fixed dipole was mounted in the centre of the reflector, the latter being adjustable between 0 and 90° vertically, and a pulse power of 8 kW at 3750 Hz was generated on a frequency of 565 MHz. A circular timebase representation was employed with a range calibrated cover glass, deflection being made to the outer perimeter.

Following the development of the *Würzburg A*, its successor, the *FMG 39 T/B Würzburg B*, incorporated a supplementary infra-red system which, while great things were expected of it, was nevertheless beset with problems and never went into production.

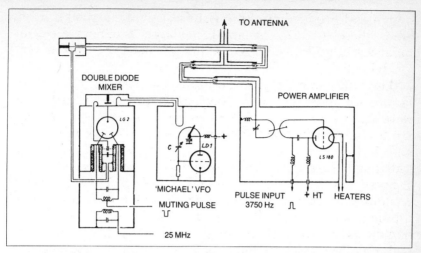

Figure 13 Würzburg A with 'Michael' variable frequency oscillator to give a frequency 'swing' around a central frequency of 560 MHz (*Fritz Trenkle*).

Runge's *Quirl* was, however, used in the following system, the *FMG 39 T/C Würzburg C*, which generated a rotating lobe around the axis of the reflector to provide a wider capture area, and another benefit was that the new direction-finding circuitry, together with the *Quirl*, could be easily produced without delaying production of the *Würzburg A*. In fact, to the credit of the Telefunken team, they designed a new display unit for this model which included a new overall-view screen as well as the height and bearing screens, these being mounted one above the other with the height-finding screen placed above the drive mechanism. The system was designed for two-man operation and was very successful. Time-base clipping and phase-conversion produced a 'dark point' on the overall-view screen on which the target was displayed, and the bearing accuracy was improved to ±0.5°, an achievement that proved itself many times in active service. So fast was the production of this model that by June 1941 over 70 were in action.

Although the Flak were reasonably satisfied with this improved bearing accuracy, they still clamoured for improved range measurement, and in response to this Telefunken produced the *FMG 39 T/D Würzburg D*. This was actually nothing more than the *Würzburg C* with an improved range-finding system added, but this *D-Addition*, better known in higher circles as the *EAG 62 Emil*, while of fairly simple design, was most effective in bringing about a substantial improvement in range measurement accuracy of about 25

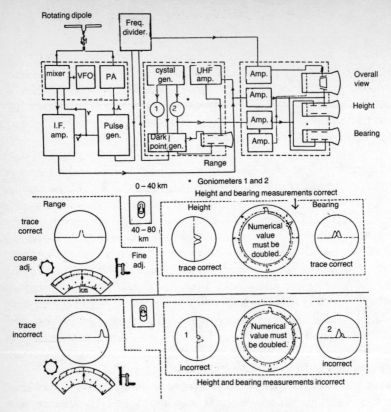

1. Paraboloid must be swung higher until both peaks are at the same height.
2. Rotating platform must be swung to the right until both peaks correspond in size.

Figure 14 Block layout of the Würzburg Riese (*Fritz Trenkle*).

metres. This was further improved by the substitution of a reference trace for the 'dark point' which was adjusted by the controls of a phase-conversion system whose coarse and fine goniometers had a gear ratio of 8:1, these being mechanically coupled to another system over which the data was fed to the Flak battery. From 1942 this system was incorporated in the greater part of all the *Würzburg* series, and by the end of the war over 4,000 equipments had been introduced.

In 1941 the High Command began to get concerned about the increasing number of RAF raids and called for a radar with an even better range and bearing accuracy to be used in conjunction with the Navy's *Freya*, the two being chiefly required for nightfighter guidance. Accordingly, Dr Pederanzi with the assistance of Dr Neubauer[1] drew up a design for an equipment with a 7.5 metre diameter parabolic reflector of

---

[1] Technicians in Professor Brandt's team.

lattice and girder construction, but as this larger version, the *FMG 39 T-R Würzburg Riese* (Giant Würzburg) called for engineering work beyond Telefunken's capabilities, they approached Dr Schmid of the Zeppelin airship works at Friedrichshafen on Lake Constance, who agreed to manufacture the paraboloids. And it was this move that helped to give the game away to the British.

In his search for the *Würzburg* Jones had discovered a number of *Freya* stations on the Channel coast, but the PRU had not yet seen any sign of the smaller radars. From their transmissions he knew they had to be in the areas already covered by the reconnaissance aircraft, and, in fact, he suspected the Germans might be setting up a nightfighter zone using these equipments in the neighbourhood of den Helder, and possibly another one near Bad Kreuznach. In fact, he already had a photograph in his hands, but was unsure about it. This had been taken in May 1941 by a member of the American Embassy in Berlin and showed a construction on the Flak tower in the Tiergarten, but there was nothing to indicate its scale, and being rather indistinct it could even have been a searchlight.

A few weeks later, a Chinese physicist who had been working in Berlin and was now on his way back to China was approached by British Intelligence officers in Ankara and persuaded to come to England in case he might have useful information. On his arrival he was treated rather cavalierly by British Security and was naturally indignant, but said he had seen the structure on the Flak tower and thought it was of a mesh construction.

Knowing that the PRU was now flying sorties over Berlin Jones was able to obtain pictures enabling him to 'relate the dimensions of the tower to those of the Tiergarten as a whole' and to work out that the diameter of the reflector must be about 20 feet. At about the same time he received information from the Belgian Resistance of the existence of a *Freya* some 35 miles east of Brussels, and when the PRU returned with photographs of this, another structure was shown in them which strongly resembled the one in the Tiergarten.

These photographs were taken by Squadron Leader Tony Hill, who in a celebrated 'dicing'[1] operation later photographed the *Würzburg A* near Bruneval. In *Most Secret War* Jones recalls:

As soon as I saw Tony Hill's photographs of the Giants, with

[1] Low level photography at great risk. Dicing with death.

their lattice-like frames for the paraboloids, I was seized by a feeling that I had seen that kind of construction before: where was it? Then, in the spring of 1943 we heard a rumour that the paraboloids were made at Friedrichshafen on Lake Constance. That was the clue: the old Zeppelin works! What I had been reminded of were photographs of the skeletons of shot-down Zeppelins in the 1914-1918 war.

On 22 June that year the works were attacked by Bomber Command and many paraboloids were destroyed.

The *Würzburg Riese*, perhaps one of the most well-constructed and reliable radars of the war (and even after it, when it was used for radio-astronomy) was mounted on a rugged 4-wheel cross-section platform especially designed for it, and employed the *Leonard* rotation system which was noted for its particular smoothness and precision. Similar circuitry to the *Würzburg D* was employed, except that the prf was changed to 1875 Hz, which gave it a range of over 70 km, and the *Quirl* was also installed. It had a bearing accuracy of ±0.2° and a height-finding accuracy of ±0.1°. As we have learned, the first of this series was installed in the Tiergarten in Berlin, but its main employment was in the *Kammhuber Line* (qv) for fighter guidance. The Navy and the Flak also used them in some places, and some were designed for mounting in railway trucks and were for this purpose re-classified as the *FuSE 65 E Würzburg Riese E*. The addition of *Freya* dipoles to each side of the *Quirl*, together with the *Freya* circuitry and display units, was a feature especially designed for installation in the night-fighter control ship *Togo*[1] off the Dutch coast. With a special stablising mechanism provided for use in a heavy sea, this was known as the *FuSE 65 G Riese G*.

Towards the end of 1941 the engineers came up with another equipment, the *FMG (Flak) 40 T Mainz*. This was in some respects similar in appearance to the *Kurfürst* of Lorenz except that it had three parabolic reflectors each fitted with the *Quirl*, but in any event it did not match the performance of the *Würzburg* for although it had a bearing accuracy of ±0.1° and a height-finding accuracy of about 0.5°, its range was only 35 km with an accuracy of about 20 metres. Tested during the winter of 1941 at the Anti-Aircraft Training Establishment at Rerik, it

[1] 5042 BRT. Built for the German Afrika-Line in 1938 she was taken over by the Kriegsmarine as a troop transport, and was also employed as a minelayer in the Baltic. Her employment as a nightfighter control ship began in 1943.

was however considered good enough for over 50 sets to be ordered, and in fact the equipment performed quite well despite its range limitation in various parts of Germany. By 1942, when the RAF stepped up their raids, the equipment had been further improved, and it gave a good account of itself, particularly in the Halle-Leuna district.

A different and gratifying experience was in store for the team on the appearance of their next system, the *FuMG (Flak) 41 T Mannheim*, later re-classified as the *FuSE 64*. This model turned out to be one of the most reliable and effective radars to enter service. Adaptable and flexible for Flak duties, rocket-guidance, and automatic bearing-finding, it contained over 100 valves and a triple screen display unit, and it functioned perfectly despite the fact that there was little time in which to develop more sophisticated circuitry. Trouble-free rotation was provided for its platform by stanchions which supported a transverse framework, on which were built all the systems for its operation. These included three parabolic reflectors and their driving gear, the power supply, main console and display unit, a storage compartment and benches for the operators.

The first of these was known as the 'A' series, which contained an additional system called an *Aquarium*. This comprised a special display in the form of a transparent map of the area on which the targets were shown as pin-points of light from tiny projectors, but this was replaced in 1944 by an electronic system which was used in the later 'B' series. The *Mannheim*'s canvas-covered cabin also housed a height-finding computer with driving gear for range-measurement and height-finding in conjunction with a mechanical ranging-map. The transmitter delivered a pulse-power of 16 kW from a pair of LS 180 pulse triodes in push-pull on frequencies between 554 and 566 MHz, while the receiver was a superhet with greatly increased sensitivity. Its accuracy was about 8 metres for ranges up to 15 km and for heights up to 10 km, and it could also supply the bearing-angle, height-angle, slant-range, map-range and the flying height of the target. Above all it had in most cases a superb penetrating power against *Window*, even surpassing the *Würzburg* on some occasions.

The installation of the combined *Würzburg/Freya* system in the Togo was by now showing some promise, and in view of this it was decided to produce a similar model for use on land. This was the *Würzburg Riese G 1A-G3*, of which little is known except that for a number of reasons, mainly concerned with its design, it only reached the planning stage and was never put on the production line. Much the same thing happened with the proposed *FuSE 66 Würzburg Riese Gigant*, a monster among *Würzburgs* with a 160 kW transmitter, but this was mainly the result of manufacturing problems. A few models were made but it was never fully developed.

A similar fate awaited the proposed *FuSE 67 Würzbach* which was a split-site design intended to protect the operators from the shrapnel of the Flak guns and the attention of low-flying aircraft, which by this time were being troublesome. The idea was to use a small *Würzburg* paraboloid at some distance from the operating position by employing remote-controlled rotation, but as this scheme called for the development of new equipment for its rotation and time would not permit this, they made an adaptation of the existing *Leonard* mechanism. This was therefore put to use in the *FuSE 68 L Ansbach I (W)*, where a parabolic reflector of 4.5 metres diameter was mounted on a mobile rotating platform operated by remote control from the operating position some distance away. As this position should also ideally be mobile, an operating vehicle, the *Bedienungs-wagen 68*, was designed (or rather adapted) in which the essential equipment was placed.

It is known that the *Ansbach*'s range was 35 km, with a direction-finding accuracy of $\pm 0.1°$, but apart from this some mystery surrounds it, as for some reason it receives little mention in official records. It is known that a few models were used in Czechoslovakia, somewhere in the neighbourhood of Prague, but for obscure reasons it was never employed elsewhere. To this day the matter remains a mystery. What is known is that it was the last of the large developments on 560 MHz, although a number of additional models were based on it and never came to fruition. These included an attempt to combine a *Freya* addition for fighter guidance with the *FuSE 69 Ansbach 2 G*, but this proved unsatisfactory, and a similar fate overtook its successor, the *FuSE 69 S Ansbach 2 (S)*, in spite of, or because of, its 160 kW transmitter and somewhat involved circuitry, and a brave attempt to use the components of the *Mannheim* in a version known as the *FuSE 70 Ansbach 3* was also unsuccessful despite the hopes held for it.

Perhaps the only really successful model was the *Ansbach Grau* which was designed for fighter guidance, and which worked on a range of frequencies between 335 and 430 MHz. This gave very good service in action before it was replaced by more improved systems.

It is understandable in view of the success of the *Mannheim* that attempts should be made to incorporate with it other systems, but its combination with the *Freya* to produce the *FuSE 73 Koburg 3* was singularly unsuccessful. Slightly better results were obtained with the *FuSE 71 Koburg I G*, which, being very similar to the *Würzburg Riese G 1* and with a 160 kW transmitter, was also designed for installation in bunkers below ground (the antennas being above of course). And in an effort to find a favourable compromise between capture-angle, range, and precision direction-finding, in order to be less dependent on the *Freya*, the Naval *Seetakt* was even pressed into service and combined with a few of these systems to make a pair of models known as *Grauechse* and *Schwarzechse* (Grey Lizard and Black Lizard). These operated on the *Seetakt*'s frequency of 368 MHz, but were found to be not of great value.

By 1942 the RAF had got into its stride in bombing raids on Germany, and the constant increase in aircraft speed and height brought fresh problems, especially for the Flak. The range and striking accuracy of the batteries was seriously impaired, and consideration had to be given to other forms of defence from the ground. To this end anti-aircraft rockets were designed, which promised a degree of success, but they demanded precise guidance systems and an equally precise radar equipment.

To avoid wasting time on a completely new development, especially as these raids were now having an effect on the industry which, in any case, was also heavily overburdened with other electronic commitments, it was decided to combine the *Mannheim* with the platform and antenna system of the (up to then) unsuccessful *Würzburg Riese Gigant*. This marriage resulted in the *FuSE 75 Mannheim Riese Bamberg* which gave much better resolution of the target by also employing an optical range-finder coupled to the rotation system of the reflector. Compared to the *Würzburg Riese* this combination not only had a longer range, but a considerably improved direction-finding accuracy of ±0.07°. This was a great step forward in precise location of the target, and the development team were rightly proud of their efforts. Nevertheless, the guidance of the rockets still had to be synchronised with target-location, and for this a system was developed with a second measuring device which incorporated twin range and direction-finding facilities so that both the target and the course of the rocket could be tracked. This ancillary system was called the *FuSE 75 RF Bamberg RF*, and gave excellent service in spite of sometimes severe operational problems during the raids.

At the same time Pederanzi's team – now enlarged by the introduction of once-retired technicians and scientists – (the strain on the industry was growing more pronounced day by day) were having second thoughts about the limitations of the *Mainz*. It seemed a waste to neglect its superb circuitry if there was a chance of using it in another capacity, and it might serve very well, after modifications, for an automatic range-following system. Accordingly, it was re-designed and fitted with the rocket-tracking system *Russelheim* which had been tested at Peenemünde for use with the V2 rockets.[1] It was with great relief that the team discovered this arrangement to be highly satisfactory, and filled with a sense of achievement, they undertook further development of similar systems on higher frequencies (mainly to beat the British jamming) which had the added advantage of requiring much smaller parabolic reflectors.

As by now the High Command was in no doubt as to the merits of radar for defensive purposes (and, in fact, could not get enough of it) the problem of British jamming had to be dealt with. A meeting was therefore held of responsible authorities to discuss what measures could be taken, and it was laid down that more flexibility of frequencies should be introduced. Clearly, the existing frequencies of 560 MHz for the Flak, 125 MHz for early-warning, and 368 MHz for naval gunnery must be made capable of a wider tuning range, and this entailed the development of broadband antennas. A start on broadband antennas had in fact been made before the war, but had been curtailed in view of the then widely held belief that such a defensive measure would not be required.

Dr Leo Brandt, now Head of Telefunken's radar research team, at once instigated a series of experimental developments under the code-name *Wismar*. This was a range of frequencies for use in a series of inter-related wavebands known as *Inselwellen* (Wave-islands) which, through the employment of broadband antennas, would allow a swift change of frequency at any time that enemy jamming occurred. It was estimated that the development of broadband antennas would take about two years at the present rate of production, although it might be speeded up if more manufacturing capacity could be found.

Runge's directional radio link system *Michael* was found to be

---

[1] V2 (*Vergeltungs* = Retaliation) was a propaganda term. The official designation was the *Aggregat 4* (A4).

of additional service here, for its variable frequency oscillator was used to replace the fixed oscillator of the 560 MHz Flak radar systems, thus allowing a 6 MHz swing either side of this central frequency. This system was designated *Insel A* (Island A) and was swiftly followed by *Insel B* which permitted a similar swing around a frequency of 530 MHz, and *Insel C* for 490 MHz. By a stroke of good fortune extra capacity had swiftly been found for the manufacture of broadband antennas, and these came in time for all three systems.

In the case of the *Würzburg* equipments, which also operated on 560 MHz, another transmitter specially designed for broad tuning, with a similar receiver system, had been tested and introduced under the code name *Urechsee*, and a similar system for the *Mannheim* series was also adopted. The efficiency of the entire network of systems was such that by March 1943 enemy jamming could be overcome by frequency changes within an *Island* in twelve seconds and, if need be, from *Island* to *Island* in well under half a minute.

This idea was of course all very well if the enemy did not resort to variable frequency jamming transmitters. In fact, they did just that by employing receivers which automatically scanned the spectrum for frequency changes, and then tuned the jamming transmitter to them. The result of this countermeasure brought about an immediate need on the German side for systems employing almost continuous frequency alterations, which not only meant more production time, but also impeded the versatility and usefulness of a deal of radar systems. Before such measures had to be made, a method was devised by Dr Hoffmann and Dr Heyden for improving searchlight radar. This entailed the phase-conversion of the time-base and the focusing of the reflectors on the height-trace, but it was further developed so that a range-finding method with accurate direction-finding was possible through the filtering out of the polarisation of the enemy transmitter. These systems were known as *Stendal B* and sometimes as *Goldammer* (Yellowhammer).

On the night of 23 July 1943 British bombers attacked Hamburg and for the first time dropped *Window*. The Germans calculated that over 92 million strips must have been used, and these effectively blinded all the radar defences. In fact, the Flak used over 50,000 rounds and shot down only three aircraft. But *Window*, was no secret as Runge has mentioned, because it was at first the subject of experiments by Roosenstein and further developed by Dr Stuber and Dr

Schulze at Rechlin, until Göring, frightened of retaliation, forbade any mention of it.

The sequel to the employment of *Window* was a total unpreparedness on the part of the German electronics industry that nearly, but not quite, broke it.

From the British viewpoint *Window* has a turbulent history and is worth recounting here, because apart from its effect on the Germans its repercussions were also felt among the corridors of British power, and even today its echoes have not completely died away. Let Jones take up the story:

> In June 1937 I paid my first visit to Bawdsey[1] at Gerald Touch's invitation and with Watson-Watt's approval. I had already guessed what they were doing, since the radar equipment on the liner *Normandie* had been described in the press ... a weakness occurred to me when Gerald Touch[2] said that the method was so sensitive that it could detect a wire hanging from a balloon at forty miles. All one might therefore need to do to render the system useless would be to attach wires to balloons or parachutes at intervals of half a mile or a mile, and the whole radar screen would be so full of echoes that it would be impossible to see the extra echo arising from an aircraft.

At this time Jones was undertaking research into infra-red detection methods (his appointment to the Air Ministry came in 1939) and on 2 July the Air Defence Research Sub-Committee reported that 'Considerable progress has been made. Work should continue in view of the possible application of the results to other problems.' These 'other problems' became clear a few weeks later when Professor Lindemann, Churchill's scientific adviser, told Jones that the Committee were going to shut down his work.

> I replied that infra-red certainly had its limitations of not being useful through cloud and of not giving an indication of range, but that radar, too, was vulnerable, especially to a 'smoke screen' of spurious radar reflections which only need be lengths of wire half a wavelength long. Lindemann told me that he would get Churchill to raise this point at the Sub-Committee. When I subsequently asked him what had

[1] The site of Britain's first radar experiments, 1936.
[2] Dr Touch, a friend of Jones from his Clarendon days, joined the radar team about this time.

happened he said that Tizard and Watson-Watt had rather 'looked down their noses' at the suggestion.

Years later, when Dr Alfred Price was writing *Instruments of Darkness*, he found a memorandum in Lindemann's files, dated 8 March 1938:

> Lest too much reliance be placed on RDF (radar) methods it is perhaps worth pointing out that certain difficulties may easily be encountered in actual use.
>
> Though undoubtedly excellent for detecting single aircraft or squadrons thereof, flying together, it seems likely that great difficulties may be encountered when large numbers of aeroplanes attacking and defending are simultaneously in the air, each sending back its signals.
>
> This difficulty may be very materially increased if the enemy chooses to blind the RDF operator by strewing large numbers of oscillators in the appropriate region. Such oscillators need consist merely of thin wires fifty to a hundred feet long which could easily be suspended in suitable positions from toy balloons or even, if only required for half-an-hour or so, from small parachutes. As far as the RDF detector is concerned, each one would return an echo just like an aeroplane.

It is interesting to observe from these exchanges how both England and Germany were well aware of the potential hazards to radar at about the same time, and even how the reactions of scientists and Service chiefs to them were not dissimilar, though it is clear that Germany probably had more to lose by its employment than Britain. The attitude of Watson-Watt in particular hardly qualified for an award on how to win friends, even if his methods could influence people:

> On 3rd December I again visited Bawdsey, and this time was put under pressure by Watson-Watt regarding the relative merits of infra-red and airborne radar. Gerald Touch actually worked in the Airborne Radar Group whose head was E.G. Bowen and which included an outstanding young electrical engineer, Robert Hanbury Brown. They had achieved a tremendous feat in getting airborne radar to work, and there was no question that it was going to be superior to infra-red. I had the impression, however, that Watson-Watt was not a good enough physicist to realise how slender a threat infra-red had always been to him, and something about his tactics aroused my resentment. Our

discussion, which he had assured me was 'off the record', was reported back to the Air Ministry, and it seemed that somehow he wished to get me under his direct control. He seemed unwilling to face the fact that radar, too, had its weak points. This suspicion, which could be attributed to my highly personal viewpoint, was many years afterwards confirmed by A.P. Rowe, who succeeded Watson-Watt as Superintendent at Bawdsey. Writing to me in 1962 of the *Window* episode, Rowe said, 'When I took over from W-W at Bawdsey, I found that it was "not-done" to suggest that the whole idea would not work ... What I want to emphasise is that from no one at no time did I hear a breath of anything like *Window*.'

That Watson-Watt's tactics should arouse Jones's resentment is hardly surprising when one learns the sequel to Watson-Watt's report to the Air Ministry, for with the closure of his infra-red work Jones was faced with the prospect of either working for Watson-Watt or finding other employment.

On 4 February Jones saw Watson-Watt and told him what he thought about his methods, and the result of this was that instead of going to Bawdsey to join the radar team, Jones was sent to the Admiralty Research Laboratory at Teddington as an Air Ministry representative. On 2 July he took up his appointment and was at once brought before the Superintendent of the Establishment who, 'after more or less reading the Riot Act to me' told him that he, Jones, 'would find things different in a Government establishment' and that in particular 'I would be under direct orders from my superior officer, Dr Hill.'

On leaving the Superintendent's office Hill turned to him and said, 'I'm sorry about that. Someone has been talking about you – do you know a man called Watson-Watt?' Two days later the Superintendent sent for Jones again and said that now he had been with them for two days they had seen quite enough to realise that what they had heard about him was entirely unjustified.

Reluctance to consider these radar countermeasures may therefore be traced to these early days at Bawdsey, but even in 1942 heated debates on whether to begin countermeasures and thus invite German retaliation were still under way, despite the fact that the British Navy was already jamming German naval radar, and on their part the Germans had jammed the British systems during the Channel dash of the *Scharnhorst, Gneisenau* and *Prinz Eugen*. And that the British had *Window* in the first place is to Jones's credit, as Rowe points out in his letter of 1962: 'Are you not being modest in not claiming to be the originator of Window?' despite Jones' response: 'It was such an obvious invention as to be hardly worth claiming, and in any event I had the earliest and strongest incentive for thinking of it because of the argument with Watson-Watt.'

Rowe himself provided the name. When the first trials of the metal foil strips began, Dr Robert Cockburn came into Rowe's office to report his findings and to ask what code name they thought should be given to it. Realising the deadly secrecy of the material, plus the fact that they had often been taken to task by Intelligence for using code names which were too obvious, Rowe looked round the room and said, 'What about *Window*?'

The trials carried out by Cockburn were under the direct supervision of Mrs Joan Curran, later Lady Curran, who tried 'various forms of reflector ranging from wires to leaflets, each roughly the size of a page in a notebook, on which, as a refinement, propaganda could be printed.'

> The form that we finally favoured was a strip about 25 centimetres long and between 1 and 2 centimetres wide. The material was produced and made up into packets each weighing about a pound, and the idea was that the leading aircraft in a bomber stream would throw them out at the rate of one every minute or so, to produce the radar equivalent of a smokescreen through which succeeding aircraft could fly.

Yet even with masses of Window at their disposal the British authorities persisted in their arguments as to whether it should be used. Watson-Watt's antagonism to it knew no bounds:

> ...the fact was that in 1941 and for almost the whole of 1942 we shrank from technical countermeasures, and the most generous interpretation of Watson-Watt's attitude was that he had developed a 'bridge on the River Kwai' attitude towards radar, and it hurt him emotionally to think of radar being neutralised, even German radar. Perhaps, remembering our old enmity, I was in turn committed to the idea of wrecking radar with clouds of spurious reflectors; but of course I would never have wanted to see our own radar wrecked. With some justice events were to lead to an ultimate confrontation between Watson-Watt and me on this very issue ...

In May 1942, with the Chiefs of Staff's approval, *Window* was loaded on to bombers for a raid, only to be off-loaded immediately because of another wrangle. Fighter Command's Airborne Radar Officer, Derek Jackson, had just heard about *Window* for the first time, and argued that if in turn the Germans were to use it against them, the British nightfighting force could be rendered useless. His views persuaded Lindemann, who up to then had supported *Window*, to change his mind. And naturally Watson-Watt backed Jackson.

The row continued throughout the summer of 1942, Lindemann, now Lord Cherwell, arguing that the Germans had never thought of *Window*, and to scatter it on them would bring instant retaliation as soon as they had copied and mass-produced it. Jones disagreed with this opinion, arguing that if the Germans had radar, then they almost certainly had the antidote to it, and went on to reveal an agent's report that a German auxiliary airwoman had chatted about the German *Düppel* experiments. Cherwell demanded to know whether Jones thought that British strategy should be based on what some woman had gabbled about, and was taken aback when Jones replied in the affirmative. Jackson was one of those asked to calculate how much *Window* would be required to knock out the German radar, and came up with a figure of 84 tons, adding that in his opinion the Germans would need only one ton to blind British radar.

At his point Watson-Watt argued that he thought Jackson's figure was too low, though he agreed that one ton was sufficient for the Germans' purpose. He added that no radio or radar device was more than 20 to 30% efficient in its early stages, and therefore Jackson's calculations should be multiplied by at least three for effective use. Jones pounced on this statement almost before Watson-Watt had finished. Turning to Lord Portal, the chairman of the meeting, he demanded:

> Are we to accept this, sir? S.A.T.[1] (Watson-Watt) has said that no electronic device in his experience is more than 20-30% efficient in the early stages of its use. If so, why does he apply this to our use of Window against the Germans, but not the German use of *Window* against us?

For a moment Portal was nonplussed and turned to Cherwell for clarification, who spelt out the meaning for him.

Portal looked sharply round, pointed his finger at

[1] Scientific Adviser on Telecommunications.

Watson-Watt and said, 'S.A.T., you're clean-bowled!' To
Watson-Watt's credit, he replied 'Not bowled, sir, but caught
at the wicket, perhaps!' and that was the end, or almost the
end, of the argument that had started between us nearly six
years before, for Portal would have no further debate. He
said that he would go straight to the Prime Minister to ask
permission to use *Window* as soon as possible, which was
understood to be 1st May.

The final meeting about *Window*, over which Churchill
presided, revolved around the question as to whether Fighter
Command would be able to carry out an efficient defensive role
if the Germans retaliated with their *Düppel*. Sir Trafford Leigh
Mallory, Chief of Fighter Command, thought that 'even
though his defences might be neutralised' the advantage lay
with saving the casualties in Bomber Command, and that 'he
would take the responsibility'. 'Very well,' said Churchill. 'Let
us open the *Window*!'

Apart from the great loss of life and the material damage done
to Hamburg, the German electronics industry, already
seriously overburdened, was forced to take immediate steps to
combat the menace of *Window*. The German High Command
was in any case astonished that the British had not employed it
much earlier, but it is clear that Göring's attitude regarding
the secrecy of *Düppel* was based on the same arguments about
its use which had prevailed on Britain, and for over a year both
sides had hesitated to use it against one another for fear of
retaliation.

One of the earliest German countermeasures against *Window*
was designed by Dr Fack and Dr Pohlmann, both at Rechlin,
with assistance from Dr Hoffmann of Telefunken. Based on
the principle of the Doppler Effect, the target echo was mixed
with a constantly running oscillator whose frequency was
synchronised with the transmitted pulses. This was known as
the *Doppler Laus* System, *Laus* suggesting the to and fro
movement of the louse as implied by the strips of *Window*, and
was intended to distinguish between the echoes received from
these as opposed to the steadier target of the bomber.
Experiments with a similar system had in fact begun in 1940 in
order to discriminate between ground echoes and true aircraft
returns, and had led to a development known as Moving
Target Indication which, even in its laboratory stages, was later
found to be useful against *Window*. The improved system was at

once applied to established radars and called *Würzlaus*, or *Freya-Laus*, and so on.

The 'Propeller Modulation' effect observed by Lorenz before the war was also adopted by Dr Hoffmann, in co-operation with Dr Kinder and Dr Scholz of Lorenz, to make a system which employed amplitude modulation transmissions whereby the airscrews of the target produced a similar effect, and the resulting echoes could therefore be distinguished from those of *Window*. Used in conjunction with the *Doppler Laus System*, the method was often of great value.

While this system was being researched an idea was put forward that aircraft echoes could be detected more strongly than those from *Window* if a form of rotating polarisation was employed. This was based on the assumption that if the transmitter and receiver used cross polarisation, the effect of the *Window* would disappear, but this method, code-named *Kreutzotter* (Viper), although subjected to exhaustive tests in 1944, failed to give useful results. Similarly, a method known as the *Taunus System*, devised by Dr Kettel and Dr Hilden at Rechlin, in which discrimination between *Window* and the aircraft was expected through a differentiation of the angle-incidence of both forms of echoes, never achieved the success hoped for.

Notwithstanding the heroic efforts of the electronics industry very little real success attended the systems they devised. The laboratory research and subsequent development right up to the production line took many months, and even then the operation of the equipment was complicated. It is true to say, however, that certain radar systems, especially those to come later, had in fact a superb penetrating power through *Window*, but by the time they appeared the war had long been lost. German scientists and Service chiefs admitted that the invention and use of *Window* remained one of the most potent weapons of the Allies against the German defences.

To return to radar design and manufacture, in 1943 the Valve Development Department of Telefunken under Dr Steimel and his team, produced valves for 27 cm operation. This was in response to an urgent demand by the Navy for the development of a Flak radar (c.f. Kühnhold's earlier declaration ...) with 30 kW of power and to include an improved display unit. Despite severe setbacks at this time due to production difficulties, plus the loss of several key operatives in a bombing raid, Telefunken not only produced this system, code-named *Euklid*, but went on to manufacture a similar system for the Luftwaffe called the *FMG (Flak) 45 T Mannheim K* or *Rastatt*. This was a rather clever design which used the *Euklid* circuitry and the display unit of the *Mannheim*, together with an improved version of the *Mannheim's* platform.

These systems were followed by a variation of the standard design which, as the result of careful planning, incorporated a new direction-finding technique, and was called the *Regensburg*.

This was followed by an improved version of the *Euklid* which produced 90 kW, and after much discussion it was decided to use this with the platform and 4.5 metre diameter reflector of the *Ansbach* to form a new equipment called *Bayreuth*, which in turn became the forerunner of the *FuMG 75 Kulmsbach* with a range of up to 120 km. For reasons never satisfactorily explained, the Luftwaffe showed little urgency to acquire this particular model, and as a consequence it saw very little action.

In 1942, as the war had lasted longer than expected, a shakeup of the military leadership took place, and, together with his other duties, Martini found himself responsible for the development and production of centimetric equipment, especially receivers. His first priority, however, was the development of a transmitting valve for 1 cm with a power of 1 kw, and this had to be capable of operation over a wide range so that a number of frequencies could be selected for tactical employment. But before work could start on it a ridiculous controversy arose. On 22 November Runge and Dr Rottgart organised a demonstration of the latest *Würzburg* to suggest that 50 cm might not, after all, be the best wavelength for this particular radar. There was a theory that centimetric waves around this wavelength were not entirely reflected, but in some cases 'mirrored away' in other directions,[1] and this theory was also upheld by Dr Esau in the Physics Technical Department.

What started, therefore, as a purely academic discussion soon grew to a serious dispute and resulted in the closure of Dr Ilberg's VHF and UHF Department a week later. Even Martini

---

[1] Objects in the path of a radar beam will cause partial scattering of the energy, the amount scattered depending on the shape and size of the object, but usually it will be scattered in all directions. Targets are therefore detected by that portion of energy reflected back along the beam from what is called the *effective echoing area* or *radar cross-section*, being the area which absorbs all the energy directed upon it and re-radiates it uniformly in all directions in order to produce at the receiver the same signal as the target. It must be borne in mind that these early days of radar led to arguments on both sides regarding the usefulness of centimetric waves.

was affected by it and declared that 'because of the negligible chances of success' and the 'strained personnel situation' work on the 1 centimetre project should cease, and that it was not worth going ahead with similar experiments in this field. This in spite of the recruitment of over 9,000 retired electronic specialists[1] who were to work on this and subsequent developments.

There can be no doubt that this controversy about the effectiveness of centimetric wavelengths and the heated discussions which followed in its wake, was one of the most significant contributions to a major breakdown in radar development. Raging for almost a whole year, during which time several projects were left in abeyance, and some were abandoned absolutely, the arguments plunged a great number of groups, teams, and whole departments in disarray, and loyalties which, up to then, had been firm and unwavering, now began to shatter under the combined strains of production needs for the war effort, and the efforts of working in wartime conditions.

Martini's announcement, coming when it did, straightaway left the industry in even greater confusion; matched only by Martini's own bewilderment at the reaction to a statement that was intended to smooth ruffled feathers. This state of affairs was, however, merely a prelude to an even greater shock which had the effect of not only settling the question of centimetres, but of bringing the industry to its senses. For on 3 February 1943, barely a fortnight after Martini's order, a British bomber was shot down near Rotterdam and found to contain not only 9 cm equipment, but a system for generating centimetric waves called a cavity magnetron. This device was immediately code-named *Rotterdam*. And its effect on the industry and High Command is best summed up in Dr Johnson's words: 'Depend upon it, Sir, when a man knows he is to be hanged in a fortnight, it concentrates his mind wonderfully.'

Göring, after reading the initial report on it, commented:

We must admit that in this sphere the British and the Americans are far ahead of us. I expected them to be advanced, but I never thought that they would get so far ahead. I did hope that if we were behind we could at least be in the same race.

The British 9 cm equipment was probably the greatest

---

[1] These were recruited from some of the Luftwaffe Research Regiments.

breakthrough in radar technology of the times. Up to its introduction British airborne radar (AI) sets worked on 1.5 metres, a wavelength which was the best that could be undertaken at the time, but which left a lot to be desired. Its maximum range was only about two miles, and its minimum range was around 900 feet, and the fact that ground returns could swamp the echoes from a target if the distance between fighter and bomber was greater than their flying heights, made this system difficult to operate under most conditions. These sets were also unsatisfactory because the beam was much too wide, with a resulting waste of energy, and they were also vulnerable to enemy jamming. The problem of the wide beam could have been solved by using antenna beams on the nose of the aircraft – the Germans, in fact, did this – but these had a bad effect on speed and manoeuvrability.

The answer was a small set working on, say, 10 cm. But this was a formidable task because of the problem shared by both sides of designing a valve for these wavelengths with sufficient power. It is the more ironic that the Germans should be considering a 1 cm valve (with the consequent upheaval) when the British were going ahead with a completely new device for generating these wavelengths.

Two physicists, Randall and Boot, at Birmingham University, came up with the idea of improving the klystron, a device in which electrons were driven through a passage of special resonators, and of employing the principle of the magnetron at the same time. The first experimental model was built in the laboratory out of odds and ends. A large electro-magnet, normally used for other experimental purposes, was pressed into service; the high vacuum required was achieved through a continuously working pump. And to seal off the ends of this infernal machine pennies were embedded in sealing wax.

The valve was first tested on 21 February 1940. A hand incautiously placed near the output became astonishingly warm, and a succession of electric bulbs used to check its power glowed at great brilliance and then burst. Eventually special neon lamps were used to show that the valve was delivering 400 watts on 9 cm. The design was placed immediately into the hands of the Research Department of the General Electric Company, whose first production model generated 10 kW. In conjunction with rotating antennas and a sweep screen Plan Position Indicator (PPI) the device was tested at the TRE's Department at Swanage, and later placed in an aircraft with the antennas canted downwards. This at once produced an 'electronic map' on the screen, in which houses, fields, forests and coastlines were clearly depicted.[1] Clearly, such a system could be used to great effect in bombing raids and in hunting U-boats.

One difficulty reared its head almost at once. To prevent its copying by the Germans should it fall into their hands, a demolition charge had to be built into it, and this proved to be useless. At Farnborough they tried the biggest possible charge, but only succeeded in blowing a ten foot hole in the side of a captured Ju88. The secret cavities of the copper block still remained for the Germans to see how it worked.

Controversy arose at once. Should this ultra secret system be used in bombers over Germany, or should it be confined to U-boat hunting where, in case of accident, the sea would hide its secrets? In the event it was decided that Bomber Command, rather than Coastal Command, could make better use of it, and, as had been predicted, a Stirling bomber into which it was fitted crashed near Rotterdam as mentioned earlier, thus handing the Germans not only an invaluable gift of both new and vital technology, but a much needed boost to the morale of their technicians and their dispirited industry.

As mentioned, this device was called H_2S/ASV. And even today controversy is to be found in some sources as to how it got this name. The true story is as follows.

Jones of course knew about the device and heard that TRE had given it the initials *T.F.*, which he at once guessed stood for 'Town Finding'. (Both the British and the Germans were often too clever with their code names.) After pointing out to Cherwell that TRE had come up with another blunder, he suggested that Cherwell ought to do something about it. As it happened, Cherwell was going down to Swanage the next day for a 'Sunday Soviet'[2], as they called their extraordinary

---

[1] Curiously enough, the pre-war view at Bawdsey, Britain's early radar establishment, was that centimetric wavelengths would not be much good for discriminating between towns and cloud fields. According to Professor Jones, the fact that towns provided unintentional corner reflectors had been overlooked.

[2] The 'Sunday Soviets' played an important part in the development of the Telecommunications Research Estblishment. Anybody, senior officers, Cabinet ministers, scientists, junior officers straight from action with one of the Commands, would meet in Rowe's office on a Sunday morning where *anything* could be said. Faults and improvements were discussed and new ideas put forward. There was nothing like them in any other establishment in England (and certainly not in Germany) and their contribution to the winning of the war was immense.

meetings, and promised to see what he could do. True to his word Cherwell raised the matter, and the scientists there discussed it over lunch. But earlier that morning Cherwell had enquired about another device thought up a year before and never mentioned since. The scientists did not like to tell Cherwell that, as he had shown little interest in it at the time, they had not pursued it, and invented an excuse. At this Cherwell exploded and said, 'It stinks! It positively, definitely stinks!' At lunch, when he had cooled down, he asked them if they had thought of another name for '*T.F.*', and someone said, 'What about H_2S,[1] sir?' Jones finishes the story:

> But they had not foreseen his obvious question: 'Now why did you call it that?' There was an awkward silence until someone who deserved to go far came up with 'Please Sir, Home Sweet Home!'

The German discovery of H_2S/Rotterdam had, as mentioned, a magical effect on the industry and the High Command. Martini in particular was prompted to an immediate *volte face*, and by 22 February the swift development of a German *Rotterdam* became the major priority of research, although this was tempered by the need for countermeasures against the British use of the system. Indeed, H_2S transmissions from aircraft over Britain were consistently heard as far away as Berlin, and thus in themselves made an excellent early warning system, but its high power presented the designers of jamming techniques with a number of problems, at least at first.

The first German-produced system was built in circumstances of a curious mixture of admiration for the British technique and a low opinion of its actual construction. To the German designer it was a constant source of wonder that his British counterpart used such (comparatively) large components on a large chassis and put the lot into an even larger cabinet. Such profligacy offended his sense of order and compactness. Small wonder, then, that the first German model was much smaller, more precise, and even more powerful than the British original.[2] And when it was tested in an aircraft the scientists had an even greater surprise, for expecting to see little more than ships at sea and coastlines, they were astonished

---

[1] As every schoolboy knows (or did) the chemical formula for the gas associated with rotten eggs.

[2] It was also 40% lighter.

when the roofs of buildings, fields, forests and other landmarks were displayed with even more astonishing accuracy.

With commendable promptitude they went ahead and experimented with the *Rotterdam* on a *Mannheim* platform, but this resulted in a range of only about 8 km, whereupon Dr Slevogt, who had just taken over control of the Experimental Department at Rechlin, mounted the *Rotterdam* dipoles in a *Würzburg* reflector and obtained ranges of up to 30 km against aircraft.

Slevogt's experiments led immediately to a complete reversal of the argument about centimetric wavelengths. On being confronted with the results of the first rebuilt model and Slevogt's subsequent experiments, those who had raised doubts about centimetres grew silent, but during that time the effect on the industry had been nearly catastrophic. In retrospect, it is hard to see why this controversy arose in the first place, although more light is thrown upon it by a contemporary of Runge who prefers to remain anonymous:

> What began as a mere academic discussion over a glass of wine grew into a mass of conflicting opinions that were never envisaged or sought after. These gave place to a frightening and scandalous situation exacerbated by the totalitarian system of government we had to endure. It grew to the stage where people were nearly afraid of committing themselves for fear of some form of retribution, and a large number of scientists were therefore led to the negative position of siding with the anti-centimetre people, in case events might prove them right after all.

Runge merely confines himself to:

> The demonstration with my *Würzburg* and other equipments was made on my initiative and with the support of Rottgart. The intention was to show that while the region around 50 centimetres was producing useful results, perhaps another wavelength might be better, and certainly not to suggest that centimetres were useless. What resulted was nothing more than hysteria brought about by the situation in which we lived and worked.

Oddly enough, this reversal of opinion on the efficacy of centimetric waves is nowhere mentioned in the official reports of the *Rotterdam* working team.

An additional bonus of the *Rotterdam* equipment was its ability to cope with *Window*, and this, apart from other obvious advantages, was the spur that drove the industry on. The Flak, of course, now had to come to terms with the new radar, for the PPI sweep screen took the place of the conventional display unit and the operators had to be trained in its use, while at the same time the name *Rotterdam* was gradually being superseded by the *Berlin* system as they prefered to call it. Having shown promise in Slevogt's experiments, it was now built on a *Mannheim* platform as before, but now employed a 12mm de-focused rotating dipole called the *Zenti-Grille*, and this development was given the designation *Rotterheim*. This radar immediately endeared itself to the Flak, not only for its direction-finding accuracy of 0.05°, but because its beamwidth of only 2° lent itself to superb *Window* penetration. From this and similar research jointly carried out by Telefunken and Rechlin during the following few weeks an idea emerged for a new and a very advanced type of radar for the Flak code-named the *FuMG 74/76 Egerland*, but its production was seriously hampered by increasing bomber raids and the problem of component manufacture. In fact, production did not begin until early 1945.

As the war situation grew more critical, discussions took place on 28 November 1944 about the development of a small series of equipments which could be hand built in small factories and workshops dispersed across the country, thus leaving the main production lines free to concentrate on other essentials. The *FuMG 76 Marbach* which emerged from these ideas was based on the *Rotterheim* and had a pulse-power of 15 kW and an extraordinary receiver sensitivity. Its range against high-flying Mosquitoes was up to 27 km, though bomber groups were located up to 35 km with a range accuracy of 25 to 35 metres. It is universally agreed that its production was the result of a creditable performance by a number of dedicated workers who often put in a 16-hour day, and even up to the last day of the war a small number of models still reached the Flak.

Only two models of the *Egerland* were produced and these were based on the *Marbach* and the *Kulmbach*. The *FuMG 74 Kulmbach*, sometimes referred to as the *Forsthaus* (Forester's lodge) contained the equipment of the airborne radar *FuG 224 Berlin* (discussed later) and is of some technical interest. The transmitter used the LMS 10 magnetron (with an effective demolition charge built into it) and pulses at 1250 Hz were generated, amplified, and delivered to the timebase circuitry. From here they were fed to the cathode of the magnetron over a pulse transformer which delivered 18 kV. Direct-current magnets provided the magnetic field for the magnetron, and a pulse-power of 10 kW with a pulse-width of 1 microsecond was delivered.

The receiver used a crystal diode mixer (ED 705) and a RD 2 MD magnetron oscillator, and the stages from then on, up to the video stages, used metal valves. The display unit comprised a PPI screen which could be switched over a range scale of 18 to 60 km, with a range-scale generator and an amplifier for the 360° point as delivered by the antenna rotation system. The antenna itself used a slotted radiator in a cylindrical reflector, and echoes resulted from a horizontal angle of 30° to the axis of the reflector. As the vertical angle was only 15°, the antenna had to be correspondingly adjustable, and a special transversing axle arrangement was provided for this.

The further employment of this remarkable gift from the British is dealt with in the chapter on airborne radar. Whether the tactical advantages of its use by the British over Germany outweighed the risk of its adoption by the Germans is still debatable. But the weight of British bombing, and the vast bomber forces which were employed in increasing numbers from that time on, played a decisive part in crippling German radar production, thus reducing the risk to more than an equal chance. On the other hand, Lt General 'Beppo' Schmid[1] and others were of the opinion that the British use of H$_2$S, particularly before the bombers reached the Channel coast, was treacherous in giving away their positions, thus enabling the nightfighters to inflict heavy losses on them.

During Jones's hunt for the *Würzburg Riese*, Squadron Leader Tony Hill was shown a photograph of a lonely house on a cliff-top near the French village of Bruneval. A few hundred yards in front of the house was a tiny speck, a dot so small that it could easily be a spot on the emulsion, yet it appeared to be round. Could this be the smaller *Würzburg* on 560 MHz for which they had been searching?

The next morning Hill returned from a 'dicing' mission with the news that he had spotted the device 'which looks like an electric bowl-fire', but that his camera had failed. Nothing daunted, he took off the following day and brought back a superb picture of a *Würzburg A*. During his examination of the picture, Jones noted that though the *Würzburg* was on top of a 400 foot cliff, there was a continuous slope down to a small

[1] Luftwaffe Chief of Intelligence during the Battle of Britain and afterwards.

beach a few hundred yards away. Turning to Charles Frank he said, 'Look Charles, we could get in there!'

I had sometimes noticed the legend 'Déscent des Anglais' on French coastal maps, recording that at some time in the marauding past British forces had landed at the indicated spots, and it might be possible to add a similar legend at Bruneval. However, I doubt whether by myself I would have asked for a raid to be made, partly because I disliked risking lives unless it was absolutely necessary, and partly because I had developed something of a professional pride in solving all the characteristics of a German equipment before I actually had it in my hands.

It had, however, been Churchill's policy after Dunkirk to annoy the Germans as much as possible by isolated raids, and as the *Würzburg* would tell them much about German radar development, the idea was passed to Combined Operations Headquarters, whose Chief, Lord Louis Mountbatten, was enthusiastic about the idea, and put the plans in hand straight away.

As a detailed knowledge of the disposition of German forces in the neighbourhood of Bruneval was necessary, signals were sent to the French Resistance. Responsibility for the gathering of this information was placed in the hands of Gilbert Renault, known only by his code-name of 'Rémy', who immediately recruited two other members of the Resistance to help him, Roger Dumont, known as 'Pol', and Charles Chauvenau as 'Charlemagne'. They not only sent back word of all German dispositions, but the fact that the beach was not mined. (Rémy survived the war, but Pol was cruelly betrayed by a congratulatory signal he received after the Raid and shot by the Germans in 1943.)

It was decided to land parachute troops to capture the radar and to use the Navy to return them and their booty to England, but the actual dismantling of the *Würzburg* called for the services of a skilled radar mechanic, and to this end Flight Sergeant C.W.H. Cox volunteered for the operation. After practising parachute jumps at RAF Ringway, he was attached to C Company of the Second Parachute Battalion, then undergoing intensive training at Tilshead. But there was a snag. Cox would be the only man in RAF uniform, and if captured, would clearly be conspicuous and call for special treatment by the German interrogators. The War Office, with all the hidebound traditional complacency which characterised its thinking, refused to put him in army uniform, with the result that apart from the risks already inherent in the operation, Cox would be subject to even more if he fell into the enemy's hands.

Before he could examine and then dismantle the *Würzburg*, it first had to be captured, and this was the task of 'C Company of 2 Para' commanded by Major J.D. Frost,[1] a Company largely drawn from Scottish Regiments, including the King's Own Scottish Borderers (Lieutenant E.C.B. Charteris), the Black Watch (Captain John Ross, Second in Command, Company Sergeant Major Strachan and Sergeant Jimmy Sharp) and the Seaforths (Sergeant Grieve) with an Engineer Detachment under Lieutenant D. Vernon. The men under Captain Ross and Lieutenant Charteris were to hold the beach, while the remainder were to capture the *Würzburg*. The total force was 120 men.

The raid was successful. The official German Report states:

At 0055 hours on 28 February 1942 the Freya radar station reported approaching enemy aircraft NNE at a range of 29 kilometres. The parachutists were spotted by ground and communications personnel of the Army and the Luftwaffe at 0115 hours, and the landing which was carried out in complete silence was south east of the objective.

All positions were at once alerted, and scouts sent out to reconnoitre returned with the information that the enemy was moving from southwards towards the objective and had split into several groups.

The reserve platoon of the First company 685 Infantry Regiment had completed an exercise shortly after 0100 hours when the parachutists were sighted, and the commanding officer made immediate contact with the Bruneval Guard, whose sergeant had already put his men on standby. The platoon reserve at Bruneval was ordered to occupy Hill 102 to the south east of Bruneval, and the commanding officer of La Poterie platoon then led his men towards the château.

On reaching the farm buildings north east of the château the German troops came under fire from the British Commandos machine-guns, and they engaged the Commandos from the west end of the buildings. The Commandos were already in possession of the *Würzburg*. Here one of the Commandos fell. This German platoon also came under fire

[1] Now Major-General J.D. Frost

Above R.V. Jones at the Clarendon Laboratory circa 1936 (*Prof R.V. Jones*)

Right Professor R.V. Jones (*Prof R.V. Jones*)

Above Leutnant Diehl's *Scheinwerfer-Parasit* showing the Freya dipoles mounted each side of the searchlight (*Fritz Trenkle*)

Left The *Freya Fahrstuhl* (*Fritz Trenkle*)

Right The *FuMG 451 Freiburg II* (the *Freya-Flammen*) (*Fritz Trenkle*)

Above Power amplifier and antenna coupling of the *Freya* (125 MHz) (*Fritz Trenkle*)

Left Professor Wilhelm T. Runge (*Prof W.T. Runge*)

Right Würzburg A with IFF antennas at sides (*AEG Telefunken*)

Above Power amplifier
of the 180 MHz *Freya*
(*Fritz Trenkle*)

Left Dr Rudolf Kühnhold
(*Dr Rudolf Kühnhold*)

Right Würzburg Riese
(*AEG Telefunken*)

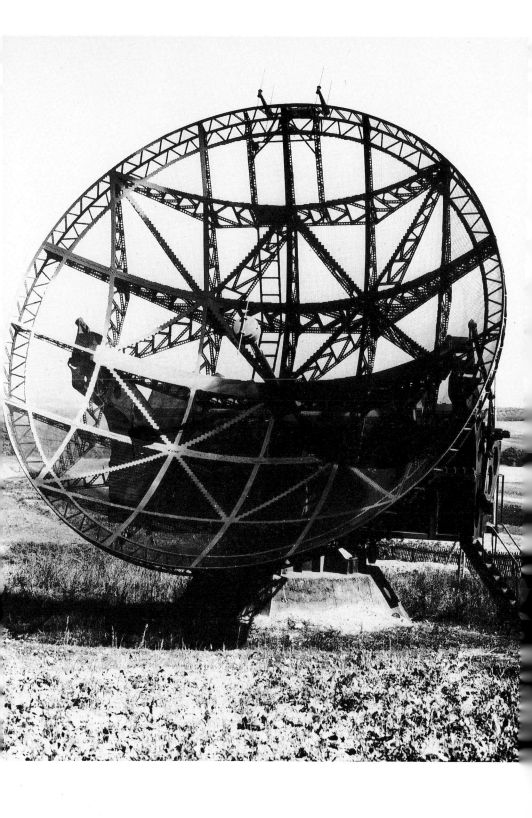

from the left flank, but the Commandos were prevented from carrying out their attack on the *Freya* position. The remainder of the Luftwaffe Radar Station unit billeted in the farm buildings took part in this action.

Acting on orders, the platoon from Bruneval village divided into two groups and advanced on Hill 102, but outside Bruneval they came under attack from Commandos who had landed north of L'enfer. Although this platoon was unable to stop the infiltration of the Commandos between Bruneval and Hill 102, it nevertheless prevented some Commandos from reaching their boats in time. These were taken prisoner along with a wounded Commando. This Bruneval platoon did not take part in the action at the château because at this time the British objective was not clear.

The Commandos embarked just as strong reinforcements from the German side reached Bruneval. The platoon from La Poterie fought their way to the Radar Station as the Commandos withdrew. The Luftwaffe personnel there had put up a stiff resistance, and only after they had used up all their ammunition were the Commandos able to reach the *Würzburg*. One of the Radar crew had been killed by a British grenade as he tried to destroy the *Würzburg* with a demolition charge. The Commandos began to dismantle the *Würzburg* and also took photographs. After this, they clearly intended to attack the *Freya* position, but the timely intervention of the La Poterie platoon prevented this.

The operation of the British Commandos was well planned and was carried out with great daring. During the operation the British displayed exemplary discipline when under fire. Although attacked by German soldiers they concentrated wholly on their primary task. For thirty minutes one group did not fire a shot, then at the blowing of a whistle they went into action.

The German Army lost two killed, one wounded, and two missing. The Luftwaffe lost three killed, one wounded, and three missing. The British losses were two killed, one wounded, but managed to reach the boats, and four were taken prisoner.

It is no exaggeration to say that after examining the *Würzburg* the British received quite a surprise.

Even on the way home in the boat D.H. Priest, a radar specialist from TRE who had gone on the mission, had had

time to examine it, and during an exchange of opinions with
Cox came to the conclusion that the Germans had been making
it for a long time, possibly even ten years.

Cox, who had been in radio all his life, thought the *Würzburg*
was a 'beautiful job',[1] and was particularly impressed by the way
it made use of unit construction for easy fault-finding and quick
replacement, a view also shared by Jones.

The *Würzburg* operator had been taken prisoner and was
very co-operative. But as Jones points out:

> Before the equipment went to TRE at Swanage for detailed
> examination, we took some of it out to Felkin's[2] Headquar-
> ters, to discuss it with the operator who had been taken
> prisoner, and who was very co-operative. We were
> disappointed that despite his readiness to help, his technical
> competence was far lower than that of any of our own
> operators. In fact, up to that stage in the war, he had had
> more time in jail than out of it. We spent the afternoon
> sitting on the floor with him, fitting the various pieces
> together, and listening to his comments. On his last leave he
> had remarked to his wife that his station was so isolated that
> the English might easily make a raid and capture it, and he
> was now wondering whether she might have been a Fifth
> Columnist.

The low technical competence of the operator and the high
engineering standard of the equipment were closely associated.
After the war, Jones met Martini and expressed his surprise at
these two factors. Martini explained that he had a very low
priority for demanding radar personnel and had to put up with
those deemed unsuitable for other duties. There was no skilled
reserve to draw upon among radio amateurs, as the British
had, because Hitler had banned amateur radio before the war.
The equipment had therefore to be made so well, and so easily
replaceable if any part broke down, that the system could be
operated by relatively unskilled personnel.

The superiority of the engineering standard was indeed
much higher than the British systems, and to ensure that no
lack of morale appeared in engineering and (later) public
circles, a story was disseminated (and still believed by some

---

[1] Cox. Letter to the author.
[2] Squadron Leader (later Group Captain) Denys Felkin was in charge of
prisoner of war interrogation and captured documents.

today) that German radar was much inferior to the British.[3]
That this was wildly inaccurate is however attested by those who
at the time were in possession of the facts, as Jones points out:

> ...the stability of every German radar station was better than
> that of the best instruments we had available to check them.
> In fact, Martin Ryle, afterwards to win a Nobel Prize for
> Radioastronomy, was one of our observers, and he told me
> that ever afterwards if he wanted to know whether a radar
> transmission was British or German, all he had to do was to
> check its stability.

To achieve and maintain these standards, and even to improve
upon them in the face of political and military dissension, and
in spite of severe disruption of the production lines from Allied
bombing, to say nothing of the strain of a war economy, must
remain for all time a tribute to the skill and determination of all
those involved in the German radar programme.

---

[3] While it is true to say that the British radar programme was the most
vigorous, creative and effective, it by no means follows that the actual
equipment was always superior.

CHAPTER FOUR

Early Warning Radar

As soon as Martini learned of the success of Kühnhold's *Freya* he demanded that it should also be assigned to the Luftwaffe for early warning purposes, and at the beginning of 1939, after much wrangling, an equipment was handed over and eventually erected in Czechoslovakia to see if its performance over land, particularly rugged terrain, was equal to its success over the sea.

With a fair degree of logic, the Luftwaffe Signals Troop, who were given the responsibility for its erection and testing, thought the best site was on top of a mountain and therefore chose a peak in the Sudeten range for the purpose, only to find the receiver swamped by echoes from nearby mountains and forests.

After some deliberation, they decided to dig a hole and place the *Freya* in it with the antennas just above the surface, and while this certainly reduced the unwanted returns to a minimum, it was still obvious that a great deal of work and experimentation was called for, and they persevered at their task for several months until they achieved a fair amount of success. In fact, this early work was to have useful repercussions later on in the war.

During this period Gema further improved the system by providing two rows of six dipoles mounted one above the other for transmitting and receiving, these being arranged on top of a new circular operating cabin. By the middle of 1939 this was even more improved by a mechanism for raising or lowering the antennas electrically or by hand. At the same time they designed an even better cabin, this time rectangular in shape, which was mounted on wheels for easy transportation. This model was called the *FMG (Flum) 39 G (gB) Dete 1 Freya*, and with 8 kW of pulse power and a prf of 1,000 Hz the range was 150 km, formations of aircraft being easily detected under most conditions at this distance, and single aircraft up to about 70 km.

As by now the RAF were beginning to make their unwelcome presence felt, it became obvious that radar would have to play an even greater part in the defence system. The Germans did not know, of course, that the RAF were forbidden to bomb large towns at this time[1] and had to confine their operations to shipping and harbours, but it was not long before they began to make incursions further inland, and the German High Command thought it wise to make provision for a number of radar stations at strategic positions on their coasts and islands. The usefulness of these was soon demonstrated when British bombers made early raids on Cuxhaven and Wilhelmshaven. (cf The Oslo Report)

Most of the experimental work on these coastal *Freyas* was carried out by Leutnant (later Professor) Hermann Diehl of the Radar Research Group on the island of Wangerooge, and it soon became obvious that a form of fighter-guidance would be desirable if the *Freya* could be utilised for this purpose as well.

At this time, the *Freya* still used constant maximum bearing methods, and with a bearing accuracy of only about 5° the tracking of weaving aircraft was difficult. Diehl tried to counter this by introducing a rotating VHF beacon for fighter guidance, but this had only a minimal improvement.

Gema looked at the problem, and in May 1940 they came up with a system which was hoped would give an improved bearing accuracy by sharpening the focusing of the antennas and also providing another screen in the display unit for fighter guidance, but these had very little effect on the situation. During this month the RAF carried out further raids on the ports and inflicted heavy damage and a number of casualties when their bombs fell on some civilian houses. Although this was unintentional and caused by poor aiming conditions, it prompted Diehl to double his efforts over the following months, during which time he experimented with antennas and in September 1940 introduced A/N bearings: a method in which the two halves were switched in succession so that a cross-pattern emerged. At the same time he installed a bearing measurement screen with a vertical time base line, the

---

[1] Neither side was permitted to bomb inland towns at this time.

traces from the left and right halves of the antenna being displayed on each side of the line, so that when the antenna was beaming directly at the target both traces would be of equal size. Tracking of a weaving aircraft was now quite easy, and the bearing accuracy was improved to ± 0.8°. The value of Diehl's work was instantly proved when, a few weeks later, a *Freya* at Nunspeet on the Zuider Zee was similarly equipped. Fighters could now be directed to the enemy by alternating the ranges of all aircraft and determining their bearings, and the closing courses for the fighters given over radio telephony.

Martini at once gave orders for the inclusion of A/N bearings in all future systems, and even earlier equipments, but for some reason never fully understood they were not included with the next series, the *FMG (Flum) 40 G (B) Dete II Freya* (later known as the *FuSE 80*). Their first fully manufactured appearance was with the *FMG (Flum) 41 G (fb) Freya* (later the *FuMG 450*) which was unusual in that it had two bearing measurement screens, one for an overall quick view, and the other for selecting individual targets, the bearing accuracy in this case being ± 0.5°. But not all the problems had been ironed out, for Diehl was worried about aircraft at greater than normal flying heights which appeared to fade out in the null position of the lobes. Suspecting that this problem might be overcome with an increased antenna height, he carried out experiments with raised antennas on two separate masts, to find that these not only confirmed his ideas, but actually brought about a better determination of the height.

This experiment led to the development of the *Freya Fahrstuhl* (Freya Elevator) in which the equipment was mounted on a girder system and the antennas supported by a framework 20 metres high by 6 metres wide. This was replaced later with a lattice mast on which they could be raised or lowered and re-named the *Freya LZ*. A third system, really an improved version of the *Freya LZ*, came into use in July 1943 following the swamping of a number of *Würzburgs* by massive loads of *Window*. This operated between 107 and 166 MHz and used Yagi antennas, but only a small number went into production and then only because no better height-finding equipment was available at the time.

The problem of low-flying aircraft also had to be tackled, and after the matter had been explored by Gema, they provided a research equipment called the *Tiefland* (Lowland). This was a clever idea which used a pair of *Freyas* a few hundred metres apart, one for transmitting and the other for receiving, and nearby they placed a framework carrying a set of both transmitting and receiving antennas which could be automatically adjusted to swing between 0 and 10°, the principle being based on a lower angle of radiation over a pre-determined area. But after exhaustive tests the results were poorer than expected and the system never went into production.

Nothing daunted, Gema turned to the problem of aircraft directly overhead at greater heights and came up with a somewhat peculiar arrangement called the *Freya Hochbahn* (elevated railway). This made use of an earlier Lorenz system which employed *Freya* antennas and built on a lightweight rotating platform, and a phase-conversion method generated a rotating beam at an angle of 45° to the vertical. It was thought that this continuously revolving cone of energy scanning the sky would bring about good results, and so it did during tests, but due to production difficulties it was never manufactured in large numbers.

In the meantime Diehl was in demand by the Searchlight Regiments who, at this time, had very few radars, and he developed a half-active system[1] whereby echoes received by the nearest *Freya* were also detected by a pair of dipoles on a searchlight. This was tested in July 1940 but proved difficult in operation. The situation was not improved by the absence of control co-ordination between the searchlight stations themselves – a legacy from early days when defence had low priority – and it was not until this had been put right that any progress could be made. In fact, it was not until 7 October that successful results were obtained, and then fate struck a blow when a Flak shell exploded in the Command Post where the tests were being carried out. This accident which caused many casualties was the reason why the trials were from then on conducted at the Testing Establishment at Dieren in Holland.

During this period all was not well with Gema. As a newly formed company with a mixture of civilian and naval personnel, they suffered perhaps more acutely than long-established firms from a shortage of scientific personnel, particularly civilians, who, though patriotic, were sometimes unwilling to adapt themselves to Service requirements. It will be remembered also that after Hitler came to power a mass exodus took place of scientists in many disciplines, but mainly physicists, most of whom were of Jewish extraction. And though other companies also suffered similar shortages, the

---

[1] The *Scheinwerfer-Parasit*.

situation in Gema grew no better, even though they employed university students and professors who were either too old or unfit for the armed forces. Even despite the recruitment of retired persons, most of whom gave sterling service, the situation grew worse week by week.

It was with relief, therefore, that production of the *Freya* was undertaken also by Telefunken, ELAC, and Siemens, all of whom lost no time in designing new rotating antennas for the system. It is astonishing to realise that despite the obvious advantages of these, Gema were still using stationary antennas for most of their systems, but this is perhaps understandable in view of their production problems and a tendency to conservatism amongst their designers.

A variation of the *Freya* was designed and built by Telefunken for the Navy and given the classification *FMG (Flum) 41 A (fb) Freiburg I*. Built on a much lighter framework, the *Freiburg* delivered 15 kW on 125 MHz and had a slightly better performance than the standard *Freya*, although it closely resembled the latter in other respects. A number of similar models were also produced under the name *Freiburg*, but bore different serial numbers such as the *FMG (Flum) 41 G (cB)*, later known as the *FuMO 311* to *318* series.

At the same time Gema had been struggling with another version of the *Freya LZ* which in some ways resembled the *FMG (Flum) 41 G (fb) Freya*, except that the lattice mast was now replaced with an angle-sided rotating column to support the main equipment, and it had detachable antennas and a fold-up cabin for easy transportation by air. Operating at first on 125 MHz with a power of 35 kW, this model was quite successful, and it became first in a series of 300 to be produced.

Gema's troubles grew worse after the British began jamming the *Freya* coastal installations in September 1942, and these were not helped by internal conflicts over basic designs and confusion between manufacturers and suppliers of components. Also the visits of the Royal Air Force were not particularly helpful at this time. Despite these problems, working groups from Gema were ordered to the Channel coast to install equipment for the *Wismar System* particularly on the *Island A* frequencies between 121 and 138 MHz, while the laboratories turned out equipment for the *Island B* channels from 134 to 144 MHz.

On 19 December the Radar Research Regiment at Köthen, under the directions of Dr Schulze, Dr Schmalbruch and Dr Klickermann, began to select suitable sites for the installation of the equipments, and as these interchangeable frequencies had been chosen to combat the effects of British jamming they were of course subject to extreme secrecy, and classified only by colours (*Gelb, Grün, Blau*, etc.) and followed by a code number. Gema were actually able to supply the first production models for *Island A* by the end of the year, and by 23 February 1943 the first deliveries of *Island B* were made. Owing to the problems already mentioned, and particularly to the incursions of the RAF, the *Island C* equipment for 91 to 100 MHz only appeared as late as July and, much later, the *Island D ZT* with seven frequency ranges.

In development at this time was the *Vollwismar* (Fully 'Wismar') System. This was an extension of the *Wismar* principle using an even wider band of frequencies in the ranges 120 to 158 MHz, 158 to 250 MHz, and 75 to 120 MHz. The quick change of channels within these ranges was possible only with broadband antennas, and these also posed extra production problems because although plans had been made before the war for these, they had to be cancelled as a result of Hitler's *Führerbefehl*.[1] It is generally believed that if these broadband antennas had been available earlier, radar production and countermeasures would have been simple, but this is debatable.

By now Telefunken had produced the *FMG (Flum) 42 A (fB) Freiburg II*. This still worked on 125 MHz and included A/N bearings, but it was later adapted to operate on a range of frequencies between 162 and 200 MHz and re-classified as the *FMG (Flum) 42 G (cB) Freiburg II*. This model was delivered to the Luftwaffe as the *FuG 451* and to the Navy as the *FuMO 321* and *FuMO 328*.

The *Freiburg II* was also known as the *Freya-Flammen* (Freya-Flames) and this particular radar was responsible for another foolish and often tragic episode of the war, because its frequency range enabled it to receive the British IFF frequencies in the ranges of 157 to 187 MHz, 172 to 182 MHz and 194 to 212 MHz very easily. These RAF IFF transmissions appeared on the screen of the *Freiburg* as a series of jagged edges or 'flames' as the operators called them, and although the normal radar range of the *Freiburg* was about 150 km, the enemy IFF signals could be detected at over twice this distance. Such an obvious and excellent method of early warning was too good to be missed, and though it was employed very

---

[1] 'Führer order'. Hitler had forbidden any research that would not come to fruition in six months.

extensively, it was never exploited to the full. But on the British side a curious situation existed.

Up to 1941 it had proved difficult to get RAF Bomber Command to take scientific aids seriously, whereas Fighter Command was only too keen to try new ideas. The complacency of Bomber Command is illustrated by a legend that had grown among the bomber crews that the German searchlight control could be upset if a bomber switched on its IFF set, the argument being that the searchlights were directed by radar which was somehow jammed by the IFF. This belief was widespread and held by many distinguished bomber pilots.

Jones did not believe the story. Not only had he heard similar tales disseminated inside the Luftwaffe about the British defences, but argued that switching on the IFF was the most dangerous thing anyone could do. Either it had an effect on the German radar control, or it did not. If it had no effect, the bombers would be relying on an ineffective countermeasure and another countermeasure which would be effective might therefore never be developed, and if it was effective, then the bomber was radiating a signal that positively identified it as British. In that case it would be simple for the Germans to develop an equipment to challenge the British IFF and thus obtain its position.

Jones put these arguments before numerous committees called by Bomber Command, and even to the pilots themselves, but without success. Bomber Command even put forward the immoral argument that the pilots should be allowed to use their IFF in this way because it would encourage them to press home their attacks when they might otherwise be inclined to think twice about them.

This was the state of affairs which existed up to the night of 5 January 1944. By then, not only had the German *Enigma* code been long broken and the British thus enabled to read all German radio traffic, but interception of signals from all German sources was a regular occurrence. Of particular interest at this time were the signals sent by the German 14th and 15th Companies of the Air Signals Experimental Regiment, as these had told the British that the 14th Company was plotting the early flying bomb trials. On the night of 5 January, however, these signals revealed that the 15th Company was engaged in something unusual, as Jones recalls:

I was telephoned by Scott-Farnie [an Intelligence Officer] to ask what I made of the messages that the 15th Company were sending. Once again, they were ranges and bearings, and I told him that I would look at the evidence that night, 5th January 1944. The messages referred to *Flammen* (flames), and they were unusual in that they gave ranges up to 350 kilometres, well beyond normal radar range. The 'flames' could be switched off, and were not under the control of the observing station, which seemed to find it easier to determine range rather than bearing. They could also sometimes be seen during the day, and from the positions of the few plotting stations we were able to locate, we realised they referred to the positions of our bombers. By a process of elimination, I was quickly able to argue that the Germans were 'challenging' and plotting the IFF sets that had been kept switched on in some of our bombers, and perhaps also in American aircraft, too.

This of course was the very danger about which Jones had warned in 1941. A year later, the Operational Research Section of Bomber Command had reported:

> There is no evidence that the use of the J-Switch (by which the IFF was left switched permanently on) has had any appreciable effects on searchlights, flak defences, or the activities of enemy fighters, or the 'missing' rate. It is known, however, that many crews think the device effective, and it should therefore be retained ... Since no evidence has come to light indicating the harmful effects of the J-Switch, the psychological effects on the crew alone is sufficient to justify its retention.

This report meant of course that in 1942 there was no evidence that the Germans were making use of British IFF transmissions, but now, fifteen months later, Jones had to be circumspect in putting his case, because his opposition to the IFF legend was well known, and unless he could provide complete proof, his interpretation of the 'Flames' might be rejected. He therefore issued the following report:

> It appears inescapable that IFF has betrayed some of our bombers. The legend about the effect of IFF on searchlights may now be reaping a tragic harvest, and future tragedies of a similar type will only be avoided by the peremptory application of common sense to shatter quasi-scientific superstition.
> While their radar remains neutralised, the Germans will probably make every effort to utilise the radiations from our

aircraft. In view of the encouragement which they must thereby have received, they will probably try other radiations should we now thwart them on IFF, and we shall therefore need to be even more circumspect than before in our use of all radio equipment which involves continual transmissions from our aircraft.

At first, Bomber Command was inclined to reject this report, but Jones was able to point to raids during the previous month where, according to the Germans'own (Enigma) reports 9 out of the 41 aircraft lost on 2 December against Berlin had been shot down because of their use of IFF, 4 out of 24 lost on Leipzig the following night and 6 out of 26 on Berlin on 16 December. This at last convinced Bomber Command, who immediately issued orders that IFF should be switched off, Air Chief Marshal Sir Arthur 'Bomber' Harris going so far as to send a signal to all units 'flaying those idiots who believe in the joss-like protection of IFF.' Even then, the treacherous 'flames' accounted for losses of more than 6% in January and 7% in February, even up to 10% on bad nights.

> Even as late as 15th February, more than six weeks after I had originally warned about the German exploitation of IFF, there were still ten IFF sets switched on in our bomber stream. And, as I had warned, whetted by this experience the Germans were now plotting every other transmission emanating from our bombers. The Command was appallingly indiscreet in its use of radio transmissions, far beyond anything that I – with my education from the Navy in the virtues of radio silence – had ever thought possible ... After the war, one of the German scientists working in the raid tracking organisation told me that he thought that we could have had no idea of the extent to which the Germans were making use of the information that we were thus prodigally providing. I could tell him that some of us certainly knew, but we had great difficulty in making Bomber Command and even our own scientists believe it.

Fortunately, common-sense prevailed in the end and the aircrews refrained from using IFF in this way.

*

To return to 1943 ... The *Freiburg II*, or *Freya-Flamme*, was to be followed by another design by Telefunken, the *FMG (Flum) 43 T Freiburg III*, and to include horizontally polarised broadband antennas with a power of 36 kW, but this had to be cancelled as the industry was overloaded with the *Wismar* anti-jamming system. In fact, the *Freiburg III* was designed to work in all three *Vollwismar* ranges, but other work had a greater priority.

They were, however, able to produce another form of *Freya* similar to the one already operating in *Island A* of the *Wismar* system, the *FMG (Flum) 43 G (fB) Freya*, and this was used extensively in France and Holland and proved very valuable. The *Freya LZ* was also re-examined by Telefunken scientists and subjected to a revision of its basic design. After modifications and improvements had been made, it went into standard production and was delivered to the Services under three new classifications for the *Wismar* system: the *FuMG 401 A Freya LZ* on 121 to 138 MHz; the *FuMG 401 B Freya LZ* on 124 to 144 MHz, and the *FuMG 401 C Freya LZ* on 91 to 100 MHz. These variations also had enlarged antenna arrays and nearly all of them were equipped with IFF systems. A later model, the *FuMG 401 D Freya LZ*, on 162 to 200 MHz, was particularly useful in some areas of Holland and Germany.

The Research Regiment at Köthen (referred to in Jones's report) were also busy at this time. Now that in some cases longer wavelengths had to be employed, the 125 MHz dipoles had to be replaced with larger arrays, and after some successful experiments had been carried out, it was decided to use Yagi antennas because these had virtually the same beaming characteristics and A/N bearings were provided very easily. They also had the advantage of being much cheaper. These new antennas worked on frequencies between 34.5 and 176 MHz, the lower range of frequencies being mainly employed at first, with all channels receiving secret colour coding for their identification. This system was given the name *Köthenwellen* (Köthen-waves).

During their work, the regiment also employed the services of the Anti-Aircraft Training Establishment, and between them they experimented with the standard *Freya* for several weeks until they came up with a number of variations which seemed satisfactory. The first was known as the *FMG (Flum) 41 G (k1B) Freya-Köthen K1* (known to the Navy as the *FuMO 341 Köthen A*) on 95 MHz. The second, which had been troublesome during tests but nevertheless proved satisfactory after modifications, was the *FMG (Flum) 41 G (k2B) Freya-Köthen* on 88 MHz, the Navy model being the *FuMO 342 Köthen B*. Later, the *Freya-Fahrstuhl* came under the regiment's scrutiny, and it was decided to modify this to operate on what was known as the

Köthen-Gelb (Köthen-Yellow) frequency of 150 MHz, and since this showed promise it led them to adapt a similar model for *Köthen-Blau* on 63 MHz. Altogether up to eight *Freya-Fahrstuhl* equipments were used and these gave good service right up to the end of the war.

As mentioned, the *Freya-Laus* was one of several radar systems converted to the *Doppler-Laus* System for dealing with the threat of *Window*, and this was developed in March 1943 at the Central Testing Establishment for High Frequency Research near Rechlin. But it became the subject of much dispute amongst scientists and Service personnel alike because its frequency was too close to that of the nightfighter radar *Lichtenstein SN2* (qv) on 91 MHz. It was argued that as the *Lichtenstein* ought to be subjected to the least jamming, the *Freya-Laus* should work on a lower frequency. Why this argument arose is unclear, because its manufacture could not have begun for several months, and even then, although emphasis had been placed on frequencies below 80 MHz (but no lower than 60 MHz) it was finally designed for the *Köthen-Grau* frequency of 53 MHz. As it turned out, this was a good choice because the system remained in operation for many months before the British discovered the change.

By this time British airborne jamming was becoming severe, and by September 1943 the RAF had developed it into a fine art. German radar frequencies could be determined from the air in a very short space of time, and to overcome this the Germans introduced a method whereby only a few radar pulses were generated, followed by a selectable gap in time of up to 20 seconds. It was hoped that this shorter period of transmission would make it more difficult for the enemy to locate the particular radar, or at least make it harder to ascertain the correct frequency. The idea did in fact have some success but it was only a matter of weeks before the RAF discovered it.

Towards the end of the war all *Freyas* were fitted with the *Freya-Laus System*, and a number of variants were also designed and employed under the names of *Tastlaus, Nürnberg, Wasserfloh* (Water Flea) and *Rohrspatz* (Reed Sparrow or warbler), and incorporated in the broadband *Vollwismar* system, their main employment being however in the *EGON* long-distance surveillance radars (qv). To what extent these were efficient is now hard to establish with certainty. What is known is that at the beginning of 1945 671 *Freyas* were still in production, and at the end of the war over 1,200 had been delivered to the Services.

The question of Identification Friend or Foe (IFF) was also paramount. The installation of such systems was carried out on all *Freyas*, and was relatively simple since by now the *Freya* had been fitted with double-beam screens. German aircraft carried Gema's *FuG 25 Erstling* system of IFF which picked up the *Freya*'s 125 MHz pulses together with its interrogation signals and re-transmitted them as morse characters on 156 MHz. At the Freya, these were detected by the IFF receiver *Gemse* and fed to the display unit, and at the same time the normal *Freya* receiver could be switched to two different frequencies as a form of secondary radar, being in this way unaffected by ground echoes or enemy *Window*. As this arrangement was in effect a considerably amplified return signal, the range of the *Freya* was correspondingly increased, so that at most flying heights ranges of 250 km were customary. The *Erstling* (to be discussed in detail later) was developed in 1941 by Dr von Hauteville at Rechlin. The original idea was that one *Freya* was employed as a primary radar for plotting the enemy, while a second acted as a secondary radar for fighter guidance, the respective positions of fighter and enemy being plotted on a map, and course directions transmitted to the fighters over radio telephony. This system was employed during 1942 on the Channel coasts with some success, but due to the overloading of the industry, and the slow delivery of components, it gradually fell into disuse.

In October 1943 the idea was resurrected. This time it was to play a part in what was called the *EGON* system (*Erstling Gemse Offensive Navigation System*)[1] for plotting the courses of enemy and fighters, but owing to difficulties with circuit design (a case of too many people trying to do the same thing) the bearing accuracy was most unsatisfactory and the idea was abandoned for the time being. Another idea tried at this time called for two stations about 150 km apart to give the ranges of enemy bombers, but not the bearings. This had the peculiar propagation feature of showing a 600 metre orbit of enemy bombers at 150 km, but a false orbit of 300 metres at 80 km, and was therefore abandoned.

The British were now jamming the radio telephony link between the ground control stations and the fighters, and this problem required the development of a command-signal system. The first method tried out was to intersperse the pulses of the *Freya* with morse characters which, on being received by

---

[1] *Erstling-Gemse-Offensiv-Navigations-Verfahren.*

the *Erstling* system in the aircraft, would result in the generation of another pulse which was picked up on the ground by another system similar to the *Freya*, but without its customary antenna, and which was made up of two equipments called the *FuSAn 730 EGON I* and the *FuSAn 731 EGON II*. This system was to all external appearances very similar to a *Freya*, but it had a special recognition receiver and antenna, a radio-telephone system (hopefully jam-proof) and a new plotting device called a *Seeburg Tisch* (Seeburg Table). Although the installation of this system was not unattended by difficulties of supply, it proved quite effective, and from April 1944 two installations could be carried out each month. Some time later another method called the *EGON-Weitling* system was tested, which also seemed satisfactory. This was designed for use in the *EGON* long-distance surveillance system (to be discussed later) where it is believed to have given good service, but proved rather unwieldy in operation.

For this reason a similar system was needed but with a simpler mode of operation, and to this end Lorenz developed a method of secondary radar with the use of command signals called the *EGON-Jagd-Anlage* (EGON Hunter Installation). This was followed in January 1945 by the *EGON-Jagd-Zwischenlösung* (*EGON* Interim Solution) which was designed around the *FuMG 401 Freya LZ* with *Vollwismar* frequency selection between 110 and 158 MHz. The *Freya* delivered 20 kW with grid-input pulsing, but this was shortly raised to 120 kW by using anode-pulsing. The IFF interrogative signals were sent out by the *Eibsee* transmitter over a special broadband IFF antenna code-named *Alpspitze I* (Alp Peak), and the returned signals were picked up by a specially designed receiver known as the *Kreuzeck* in the range 143 to 158 MHz. An encoding device called the *FuG 139 Barbarossa* permitted commands to be sent in the form of three groups of pulses with selectable spacing between each group. In the aircraft an IFF system was installed which used a simple equipment by Telefunken called the *FuG 25 Zwilling* (qv) and the *FuG 139 Barbarossa* encoder-decoder. The *Zwilling* received signals between 554 and 556 MHz and re-transmitted them on frequencies between 120 and 160 MHz after the received signals had been analysed by the *Barbarossa*. The command signals were then re-radiated and picked up at the ground control station, where the data was fed to a teleprinter and finally to a display system called *Hellmaus* (Bright mouse).

This was however superseded by the *EGON-Jagd-Endlösung*

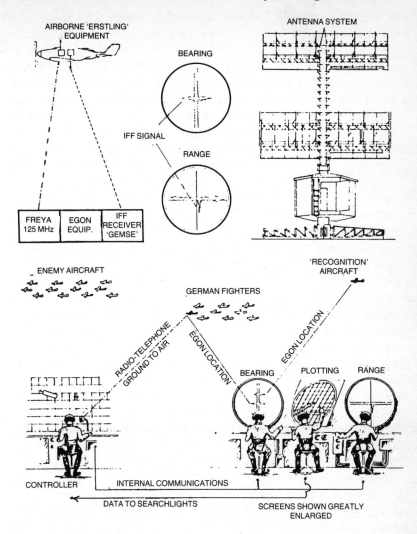

Figure 15 The Egon-Hunter system (*Fritz Trenkle*).

(*EGON* Hunter Final Solution) which keyed part of the pulses of the range measuring system *FuG 126 K Baldur K* and also employed the *Barbarossa*. The transmitter is believed to have contained the recognition equipment *FuG 226 Neuling*, but unfortunately further information is no longer available.

A parallel development was that of the *EGON B Einfachst-Lösung* (*EGON* B Simplest Solution) which employed the much smaller equipment of the *Hohentwiel-Lang* transmitter between 110 and 160 MHz (and from which the airborne radar *FuG 200 Hohentwiel* was developed). The design called for three

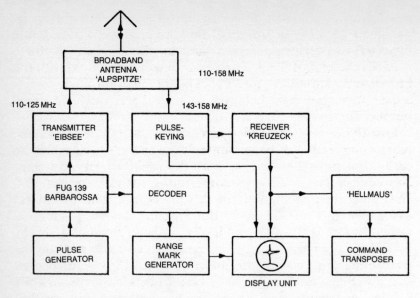

Figure 16 Layout of the Egon-Hunter interim solution system (*Fritz Trenkle*).

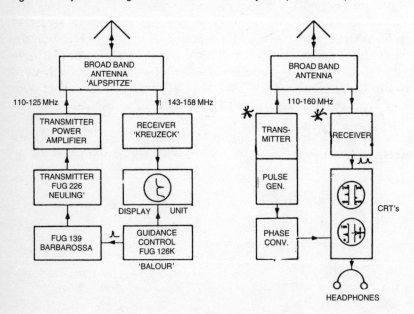

* HOHENTWIEL-LANG TRANSMITTER AND RECEIVER

Figure 17 Layout of the Egon-Hunter final solution system (*Fritz Trenkle*).

double-beam screens each using fine measurement control over phase-conversion, and the command signal encoding device *FuG 138*, something similar to the *Barbarossa*. Design development was held up on this model due to the usual problems of the war situation, but the engineers confidently expected to produce a design built on the *Kurmark* platform towards the end of 1944. Further problems associated with the broadband antennas for the system prevented its early appearance, but it is believed to have been made in small numbers in early 1945.

Low-flying raids by Allied aircraft in autumn 1944 became more numerous and troublesome. It was therefore clear that an easily transportable system was desirable to fill the gaps between the larger *Freya* stations, and as the current *FuG 200 Hohentwiel* seemed suitable for this purpose, it was the subject of experiments carried out by the Antenna Research Station at Debendorf. They used a mobile *Kurmark* platform and, on the forked arms of the mast, they erected two antennas for the transmitter and receiver one above the other. It was discovered that low-flying aircraft could be better detected if the antenna height was increased to 4 metres, and after further experiments the system came into service as the *FuMG 407 Tiefentwiel* with 40 kW of power on three frequency ranges: 544 to 565 MHz; 505 to 525 MHz, and 475 to 505 MHz. For the Navy the equipment was built on the rotating *Chinese* platform and classified as the *FuMO 64*. Another version was delivered to the Luftwaffe on the *Kurmark* platform, but with cross-over antennas and a Plan Position Indicator (PPI), and was known as the *Pantowiel*.

Some of the systems described here will be dealt with in more detail in the chapters on IFF systems and airborne radar.

CHAPTER FIVE

Long-Range Radars

Despite the pre-war opinion of pundits that Germany had no need of such systems, it became very clear after the beginning of the war that it would be desirable to have an early-warning radar with a range at least twice that of the *Freya* and, if possible, even longer. And as at this time the transmitting power could not easily be raised, experiments were carried out with different antenna configurations where it was found that by quadrupling the antenna area by using four standard *Freya* arrays, a worthwhile increase in range could be attained. These arrays were attached one above the other on a lattice mast 36 metres high, the entire construction being erected over the operating cabin with rotating bearings for the anchoring cables. The antenna array also contained elements for an IFF system and the whole assembly was rotated by remote-controlled *Leonard* mechanism.

This system was developed by Gema in co-operation with the mast construction firm Hein Lehmann and Co, the Seibert Co, and the Zeppelin Construction Factory at Friedrichshafen. It employed a standard *Freya* on 125 MHz at 20 kW, but was furnished with an extra display screen. Shifting of the vertical antenna pattern was achieved through phase-conversion. This system was known as the *Wassermann L* (Aquarius), and a small number of similar models were also designed for operation between 132 and 149 MHz.

The *Wassermann L* showed such promise that a larger system using the same principle was immediately developed. This was the *Wassermann S* which used double the number of antenna arrays on a 4 metre diameter tubular steel mast 60 metres high, and was mounted on a massive concrete base and rotated by an equally massive gear-drive system. Ten of these models were immediately erected on key positions around the coast, and, later, the transmitter power was increased to 100 kW when the ranges of the *Wassermann L* and the *Wassermann S* reached 200 km and 300 km respectively.

Such large antenna arrays on these frequencies gave rise at first to problems of feeding and matching, but thanks to the untiring work of a special team of Gema engineers these were soon overcome, and the bearing accuracy of the *Wassermann L* was increased from its former $\pm$ 8° to $\pm$ 4°, while the *Wassermann S* was slightly improved at $\pm$ 3°, the latter being later fitted with A/N bearings.

The Navy had watched these developments with a keen eye, and before long they made a demand for a surveillance radar on an even larger pattern. The Communications Research Establishment got together with Gema to produce a system called the *FMG (Flum) 41 G (fG) Mammut I* (Mammoth) which had three large frames fixed side by side to lattice masts, each frame holding an array of 16 *Freya* antennas and measuring 10 metres high by 30 metres wide, the top double row being used for transmission and the lower for reception. About 50° of lateral pattern swing was attained through phase-conversion. A set of range-measuring antennas was also placed in the centre of the array, and by means of equal-phased feeders to both halves of the sending and receiving antennas a cross-over pattern was generated in the standard manner. For longer ranges, especially for main approach paths and return flights, the system was frequently equipped with back to back antenna arrays, and with the standard *Freya* equipment this gave a range of 300 km at aircraft at 5,000 feet, but a smaller one for low-flying targets. In fact, aircraft at about 150 feet were only usually detected at about 35 km (hence the reason for bomber formations of the RAF flying at low level over the North Sea). The range accuracy was $\pm$ 300 metres and the bearing accuracy $\pm$ 0.5°, the latter being a considerable advance over the *Wassermann* systems.

As might be expected, the Navy had in fact only very few of these installations. The Luftwaffe, with the weight of Göring's friendship with Hitler behind it (as opposed to the distant formality of Admiral Raeder to the Leader) got the lion's share. The relations between the Navy and the Luftwaffe were not, to put it mildly, very good.

Shortly after the *Mammut I* came into service a number of experiments were carried out into long-range height-finding.

A team from Gema constructed an antenna array based on the *Mammut* in which the *Mammut*'s reflectors were left in place, but in front of them four sets of dipoles were arranged in ten rows and so switched that the middle, top and bottom rows gave a variable pattern. The height of the target was found by measuring a quotient of the antenna voltages over a goniometer. This system was called *Malaja*, and although it is believed to have given useful service, its range is unknown. Some commentators believe it was in the region of 300 to 400 km and this may well be the case.

One equipment of particular interest was designed by a Telefunken team under Dr Stepp. This was known as the *Würzmann*, and as the name implies, it was a combination of one of the *Würzburg* radars and a *Wassermann* antenna. Stepp believed the *Würzburg* transmitter to be more stable and reliable than the Gema design, and in fact he rebuilt a *Würzburg Riese* transmitter on a bigger scale so that it would deliver 120 kW on 560 MHz. This power was fed to a similar antenna to the *Wassermann M* (described later) which had 16 arrays of dipoles arranged side by side in vertical columns on a 36 metre high lattice mast. At the same time he included some of the antennas of Runge's directional radio system, the *DMG 4K Michael*.

After some delay caused by an administrative muddle, the system was finally erected on a special site on the island of Rügen in the Baltic, and during tests ranges of 200 km against aircraft were easily achieved. Air battles over Berlin could also be easily observed. But these distances pall into insignificance when compared to the 385,000 km distance to the moon which the system covered easily. By switching off the power to the transmitter the echo returned two and a half seconds later, and this 'party trick' was often demonstrated to astonished visitors.

Another design brought out at this time was the *Wachtmeister* (Police Constable) which was a height-finding equipment using 18 pairs of standard *Würzburg A* parabolic antennas arranged one above the other in two rows, but unfortunately details of this are no longer available.

As the production of new *Freya* combinations continued into 1942 it became imperative to equip them with the *Wismar* system. This project was a mammoth undertaking in more sense than one, for no sooner had Siemens received orders to install variable frequency systems in the range of 120 to 158 MHz than these were immediately followed by demands for 158 to 250 MHz and later for 75 to 120 MHz. This in itself was a major project, but when the original power of 100 kW was

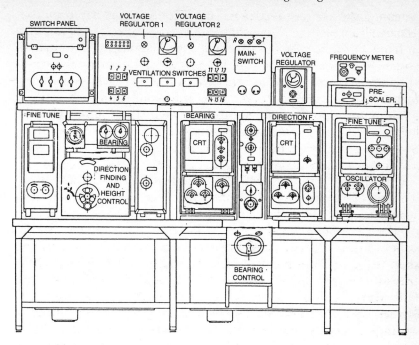

Figure 18 Layout of the *Wassermann M* operating console (*Fritz Trenkle*).

increased to 800 kW it grew to colossal proportions. It is also noteworthy that the vast number of broadband antennas required for these systems were actually built in High School engineering classrooms by an equally vast number of dedicated sixth-formers. (This may be compared to the building of American 'Liberty' ships by sixth-form schoolgirls.)[1]

One of these combinations was the *FuMG 402 Wassermann M* designed at Siemens by Dr Schultes and his team. Thirty of these systems were produced, at first still using narrow band equipment and antennas but later rapidly converted to the *Vollwismar* requirements with broadband antennas when they were known as the *Wassermann MI*. These used a similar construction to the *Wassermann L*, but employed A/N bearings and a device called a 'compensator' for swinging the vertical lobe to a null point. This comprised an antenna array of 24 frames of 6 vertically polarised dipoles and reflectors on a 36 metre mast. The success of these equipments was followed up by the *Wassermann M2* with broadband horizontally polarised antennas on a 40 metre mast. This also incorporated the *Kuh-Gemse* IFF system (to be discussed later) and its associated

[1] *We Captured a U-boat*, Rear-Admiral D.V. Gallery USN. London.

antennas. The final form of this model, however, was the *Wassermann M4* with a similar antenna arrangement on a 51 metre mast and with its operating cabin built halfway up the structure, to the discomfort of its occupants especially when the RAF were around. About 150 of these designs were delivered in the *Vollwismar Range 1* (120 to 158 MHz) with 100 kW of power, and the range over ground was 300 km and over sea 380 km, with a bearing accuracy of ± 0.25° and a height-finding accuracy of ± 0.75°.

These radars gave excellent service during the war, many of them at times far exceeding the expected ranges, when they enabled the operators to observe Allied aircraft taking off well beyond the Midlands in 'real time' and to warn the Flak and the fighters.

Towards the end of the war installations were also built for the *Vollwismar Range 2* (158 to 250 MHz) and classified as the *Wassermann M3*, and at the same time the *Wassermann M5* was designed for 75 to 120 MHz and mounted on a 60 metre mast. By a stroke of luck the Navy were able to lay hands on a few of these which were known to them as the *FuMO 331*.

By now, 1942, the British *Chain Home* System was well known, particularly to the Luftwaffe who had cause to regret its existence, but apart from serious damage to the Ventnor station on the Isle of Wight by Ju88s in late 1940 and some minor damage to other installations at the same time, the system continued to work. It seemed impossible to put the British radar out of action with either strafing raids or jamming.[1] But the Germans were not entirely complacent now about what they considered a primitive method. True, the British 'floodlighting' system was conceived during a period of dire necessity and was considerably behind the existing German technology even before the war, but if it was derided for its lower technical qualities, it was admired for the vision of those responsible for it, and the magnificent achievements of its

[1] Some commentators offer the opinion that because the Germans believed their own radar to be inferior they underestimated the potential of British radar and made no serious attempt to put British radar out of action. That this is wildly inaccurate must by now be obvious. The truth is that the Germans underestimated British radar because they believed their own to be superior. Göring stopped the raids on the *Chain Home* stations because he personally had little faith in electronic aids. 'Wars are won by men, not by equipment,' was one of his favourite expressions. And at a conference he said 'It is doubtful if there is any sense in continuing the attacks on the British radar stations, since not one of those so far has stopped transmitting.' In any case his aim was the destruction of the RAF and their airfields.

builders. Certainly the Luftwaffe was in no doubt as to its effectiveness, as they soon discovered before and during the Battle of Britain.

The British use of 12 metres (at least in the early stages) for their early warning radar had not gone unnoticed by Dr Scholtz of the Central Research Establishment of the German Post Office, who believed that a longer range was possible with careful design. Accordingly, a team under his direction produced a research model code-named *Heidelberg* operating on 23 MHz with a range of up to 400 km. It is known that the antenna system employed eight dipoles against a reflector sheet, but apart from the fact that it was used for tracking the V2 rockets no further details are available, the documents and drawings having mysteriously disappeared shortly after the invasion.

It is known, however, that the Post Office designed another model called the *Elefant* which used a *Wassermann M4* mast to which were attached six rows of horizontally polarised wire dipoles and reflectors. Only a few *Elefants* were made, and two are known to have been erected on the Dutch coast. One was also installed on Jan Mayen Island in August 1944, and it is a fact that convoys at ranges of 2,000 km were regularly located, surely making this equipment the world's first Over-The-Horizon Radar, even though it depended on temperature inversions and other propagational anomalies for this to occur. A month later this equipment had to be re-deployed due to the worsening war situation, and the opportunity was taken to make a few modifications before it was finally installed on the island of Röm in West Denmark. The system was now known as *See-Elefant* and operated between 23 and 28 MHz with broadband antennas. These antennas consisted of 12 arrays of back-to-back broadband prism radiators which were spanned out between two fixed masts 100 metres high, the transmitter being housed in the cabin from a *Mammut* installation. On both sides of this erection were installed two 70 metre *Wassermann* masts, each holding eight horizontally polarised prism antennas one above the other, this ancillary system being used for direction-finding. The initial range of 400 km was increased within two months to 4,000 km, or about the distance between England and America.

These and similar installations were principally employed for the recording of A4 rocket strikes on London at 800 km range, the end of the flight-path being easily detected. They were also used for the location and guidance of aircraft carrying guided missiles. After the loss of the flying bomb sites near the English Channel, these aircraft would approach the English coast at low level, then zoom up to launch their weapons. One such installation in course of erection near Norddeich was destroyed by a freak tidal wave before completion, but according to the documents relating to it, it had a range accuracy of 1 to 2 km (over 800 km!) and a bearing accuracy of ± 1°.

During this time Lorenz was still pre-occupied with the development of the *Vollwismar Range 2 (158 to 250 MHz)* for the *Freya*-type installations, but were also working on a research model called the *Freya-Lang-Latte* – a system based on the earlier Gema research model *Leibnitz*, itself a smaller *Mammut* with particularly good bearing accuracy – and which seemed very promising. It employed what was called a *Lange-Latte* (Long-Prop) antenna array which consisted of a frame 3.6 × 18 metres carrying horizontally polarised broadband dipoles, and the transmitter and platform of the *Freya LZ* working in the *Vollwismar Range 2*. The war situation did not permit the manufacture of this system in any large number, and from such documents remaining it appears that the direction-finding system had not been decided upon, although research had taken place into fast direction-finding with the use of the new long persistence screen *Blau-Strumpf* (Blue Stocking).

One further item of particular interest to British readers is a half-active radar system devised by Dr Wächter of Telefunken in co-operation with the Central Research Establishment of the Post Office. This equipment was actually developed in 1942 and known as the *Klein-Heidelberg-Parasit* (Small Heidelberg Parasite). And in spite of enemy jamming at this time, accurate location of bombers was still possible because it used the British *Chain Home* radar installations on the English coast for its central radiation source. Since these radiations from the British transmitters could be received very well, direction-finding from any point on the Continental coastline was a very easy matter. The line of echo-communication giving the aircraft's position was actually an ellipse, or rather, a number of ellipses, between the transmitters on one side of the North Sea and the receivers on the other (on which the target had to be) and as the exact position of every *Chain Home* station and its range of operational frequencies were known, the position of an aircraft could be found on the elliptical focal point. Reception of the main transmitted beam, which was shown as a null-point on the screen, was made by synchronised antennas and a sensitive receiver, while a larger antenna system and CRT-equipped

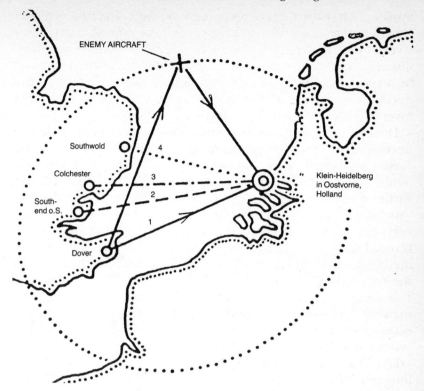

Figure 19 Representation of the *Klein-Heidelberg* principle (*Fritz Trenkle*).

rcccivcr was used for the direction-finding of the aircraft's echo.

After a number of research models had been tried near Cherbourg, a *Kleine-Heidelberg* was installed near Oostvoorne on the Hook of Holland, disguise for the apparatus being achieved by camouflaging the antennas at the rear of a *Wassermann S* installation. A circular scale on the screen had graduated marks from 0 to 40 which correspond to the number of ellipses for every *Chain Home* station, and a special map with accurately registered ellipses was also provided. The expected range of 200 km turned out to be 400 km with a range of accuracy of between 1 and 2 km and a bearing accuracy of 1°. This system gave impeccable results even when other radars were severely affected by jamming transmissions or by *Window*.

An intriguing bit of cloak and dagger accompanies the history of this system. One day a 'Leutnant' of the Luftwaffe turned up to inspect the equipment – and then mysteriously disappeared. On enquiry it turned out that though his papers were in order, no one knew where he had come from. And a few weeks later the British seemed to know about the system and tried to put it out of use by using oscillator pulse-blocking, but this was unsuccessful. It is believed the 'Leutnant' was of course a member of the Resistance, and though still unknown, his action is still all the more admired by German personnel for the risks he faced if caught.

A similar system for using British radar in the 200 MHz region was also undertaken by Gema for the Navy under the code-name *Paris*, but this project was eventually cancelled.

The British of course not only knew about the *Kleine Heidelberg* but were aware of the *Wassermann* and *Mammut* installations almost as soon as they were erected. 200-foot arrays are not easily hidden, and Jones was on the trail almost immediately.

> Later in 1942 we discovered a new form of German radar installation on the Channel coast, which was much bigger than *Freya*, and which I believed to be used for long-range detection. Because of its appearance I called the new equipment a 'Hoarding', because it resembled the kind of erection on which large bill posters are displayed on major roads; the Germans, because of its size, called it *Mammut* (Mammoth). When I directed TRE's attention to the new equipment, they listened for it and found that, as we had guessed, its radar characteristics were very similar to those of *Freya*, so that the extra performance was being obtained from the same transmitting and receiving equipment, through the extra directing power of the larger aerial array.

The experts at TRE disagreed with Jones's guesses about the new equipment and argued that it was really intended for precision long-range bombing, basing their arguments on the fact that the frequency and pulse-rate frequency were far more stable than would be required for ordinary radar. Such extreme accuracy, they assured him, would only be necessary where absolute range and bearing would be required to determine the position of a bomber relative to its target. In any case, more than one *Mammut* existed on the Channel coast, and they all had the same degree of stability.

> It was not easy to challenge the experts on matters of technical detail, when these were supported by rational argument, but I got them to agree that the ordinary *Freyas* were intended merely for radar and not for long-range bombing; I then asked them to go out and check how stable

the *Freyas* were, because I suspected that the high stability that we had observed was merely another example of German thoroughness and precision, even where it was not required. A fortnight later the experts came back and told me that I was right: the stability of every German radar station was better than that of the best instruments that we had available to check them.

In 1942 Jones learned that his old opponents, the 14th Company of the Air Signals Experimental Regiment, had recently moved a *Würzburg* radar to a place called Peenemünde on the Baltic coast, and a radar unit to the Island of Rügen just to the north. It had been suspected for some time that the Germans were developing a rocket missile, and although the movement of radar equipment might simply be a strengthening of their air defences, Jones wondered if there might be other reasons. During the autumn detachments of the 14th Company were reported to be strung out over a wide area, including another small island to the north of Peenemünde called the Greifswalder Oie, and they began to transmit over radio ranges and bearings of a moving object. To Jones's delight they employed the same code that had been used in 1941, and which had easily been broken. From the transmissions from the Greifswalder Oie, the ranges and bearings indicated that something had taken off from Peenemünde and was travelling at about 400 mph in an east-north-easterly direction. As whatever it was left the range of the Greifswalder Oie station it was at once detected by another radar further along the coast, thus making it easy to locate from the range and bearings of the track Jones had discovered.

> We could locate the successive radar stations as each plotted a part of the track in turn. The stations were usually alerted before a firing took place, and there were security slips such as a reference to 'FZG 76' and so there was no doubt about what they were plotting. It was a great moment, for my very long shot had landed us in a ringside seat at all the trials of the flying bomb.

Although from this it was clear that the Germans were probably using their new larger radar installations for the guidance and possible direction of these missiles, it later became obvious that their chief employment was, as Jones had suspected, that of long-range early-warning systems.

Long before the invasion, numbers of the new installations had sprung up on the Channel coast and inland, and were obviously detecting Allied aircraft long before they crossed the Channel. For D-Day, it was therefore necessary to know how much bombing would be needed to put one out of action.

> We decided to have a trial attack on one of the largest types of German equipment, known to us a 'Chimney' because of the appearance of the large supporting column which held the array, and to the Germans as *Wassermann 3*. It was rather like a Hoarding turned with its long side vertical and mounted on a swivelling column, and had the advantage that it could determine height as well as range.

The attack proved successful and demonstrated that the installations could be knocked out quite easily, but once the technique of attack had been established they were left alone until the plans for D-Day should properly start. The vital point about D-Day was that the Germans should be convinced that the British were going to land in a totally different place, and for this reason it would be foolish to destroy only the radar stations covering the intended landing area. In fact, it was laid down that for every attack in the proposed landing area there should be two outside it. Furthermore, it was necessary to leave a certain number of radar stations east of the Seine so that they could pick up the 'mock invasion' heading for that region, which was in fact a large and precise operation by 617 Squadron (The Dam Busters) and others, led by Group Captain Leonard Cheshire VC, in which *Window* was dropped at a certain height and at regular intervals so as to look like an invasion fleet fourteen miles wide, and approaching the coast at a rate of 8 knots. The technique was called *Spoof* and was very successful.

CHAPTER SIX

Panoramic Search Radars

As German radar development progressed it was quickly discovered that an all-round survey was difficult because the targets were shown at any one time in a fairly narrow sector, the radar beam behaving something like a searchlight pointing in one direction. On top of this, the pursuit of targets by different equipments at the same time often resulted in confusion, so for these reasons the demand grew for 'panoramic' search radars which could sweep round an area and deliver a simultaneous view of all the targets in it.

Some commentators have observed that the lack of this type of system by the Germans in the early days of the war seems to have been a remarkable oversight. Even Jones, during his search for the *Würzburg* before the Bruneval Raid, remarks:

> Our own philosophy had been to control night interceptions by means of a single radar equipment, which rotated continuously, with its information displayed on a circular cathode ray screen in which the position of the radar set itself was represented at the centre. Returning echoes were displayed along the radius that corresponded to the direction in which the radar set was 'looking'. The result was a map showing the returning echoes as luminous points which indicated the position of any aircraft within range. This device, which was so simple and obvious that we believed that anyone could have invented it, was known as the Plan Position Indicator or 'PPI'. Both the bomber and the intercepting fighter would show up as luminous points, and the task of the ground controller was to estimate the bomber's course and so direct the fighter on to its tail, assuming, of course, that information was also available about the heights of the two aircraft.

In fact, Gema had already conducted experiments and registered a Patent for such a system in 1936, but owing to more pressing commitments they could not carry out much research. But in 1940, when, as mentioned, demands for such a system were made, they conducted experiments at Tremmen near Berlin, where a large platform carried a horizontal girder 20 metres long on which were fitted 18 vertical dipoles and reflectors, the entire array being rotated by an electrical gearing system and mounted on a tower. A modified form of the feed system of the *Freya* radar was employed, and the antenna rotated at between 5 and 10 rpm with a prf of 500 Hz. All targets within an initial range of 100 km were displayed on a specially designed PPI screen 60 cm in diameter, the deflection of the electron beam at every pulse from the centre of the screen to the perimeter being achieved by sychronisation of the deflection coils with the rotation of the antenna over a three-phase system on the neck of the tube. This system was called the *FuMG 403 Panorama Tremmen*, and although the accuracy was as good as the *FuMG 74 Kulmsbach*, the larger beam-width and pulse rate frequency did not give such good resolution as expected. It was also evident that experience was needed in selecting possible sites for the equipment, as ground returns were a considerable nuisance. One benefit, however, showed itself almost immediately: it was unaffected by jamming, unless the jamming transmitter was very close.

As has been mentioned, Gema very soon became overloaded with work, and for this reason Siemens undertook much of the development from now on. They designed a new variable frequency transmitter in the range of 120 to 158 MHz with 80 kW of power, and at the same time they tested a new horizontally polarised broadband antenna which consisted of two arrays of 16 dipoles and reflectors, when the resulting range was found to be 200 km. By autumn 1942, Dr Schultes and his team at Siemens's laboratories in Berlin had further improved the design, and in early 1943 the first production model went into service under the designation *FuMG 404 Jagdschloss* (Hunting lodge). This employed a rotatable stack of 16 horizontally polarised dipoles and reflectors mounted on a tower-shaped column 7 metres high. Above this were mounted vertical broadband antennas for the transmission and reception of IFF signals on 125 and 156 MHz.

Up to the end of the war over 60 of these models were delivered by Siemens, as well as a further 18 from Lorenz which worked in the range 158 to 240 MHz, and these all came

Above General Wolfgang Martini
(*Fritz Trenkle*)

Above right Professor Lindemann
(Lord Cherwell) (*Prof R.V. Jones*)

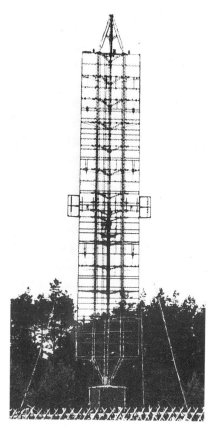

Left Freya installation on the
nightfighter control ship *Togo*
(*Dr B. Röde*)

Right Antennas and mast of the
Wassermann L with IFF antennas in
the centre (*Fritz Trenkle*)

Left Antennas and rotating column of the *Wassermann S* (*Fritz Trenkle*)

Opposite Three variations of the *FuMG 402/FuMO 331 Wassermann M*. *Left* Type M1, 36 metres high, *right above* Type M2, 40 metres high, and *right below* Type M3 and 4, 51 metres high (*Fritz Trenkle*)

Below Antennas and supporting masts of the *Mammut Friedrich* (*Fritz Trenkle*)

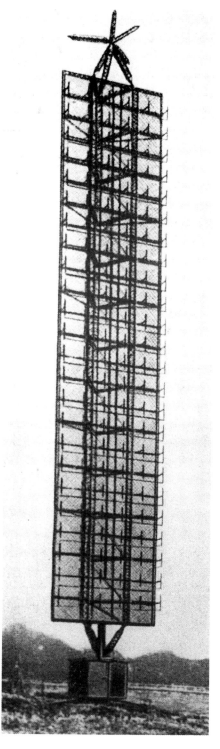

Left See-Elefant mast and array. These rotating direction-finding towers were spaced 1 km apart. Height 100 metres (*Fritz Trenkle*)

Below The first antenna for the Tremmen installation (*Fritz Trenkle*)

Above Jagdschloss installation on a brick-built cabin (*Fritz Trenkle*)

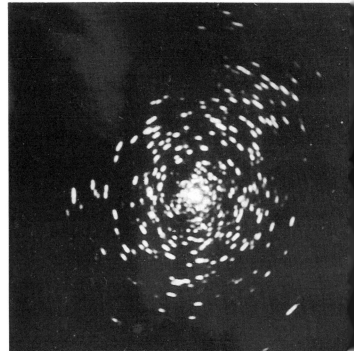

Right Screen display of the *Jagdschloss* showing targets during a night attack (*Fritz Trenkle*)

Left Antennas of the experimental nightfighter radar *Wendelstein*. Above the fuselage the transmitting antennas, at the side the receiving antenna for 'right' (*Fritz Trenkle*)

Below left Antennas of the ASV radar *Prof Scherzer* on a Ju88. The transmitting antennas are directly beneath the cockpit. (*Fritz Trenkle*)

Above right Instrument panel in a Ju388 L with the display unit of the *FuG 217 R Neptun II R* at the right, with the controls below (*Fritz Trenkle*)

Right Display unit of the *FuG 200 Hohentwiel* in the observer's position in a FW200. Inset at top right the display screen with a target shown upon it.

Antennas of the nightfighting radar *FuG 202 Lichtenstein BC* on the nose of a Ju88 R-2 (*Fritz Trenkle*)

The display unit of the *FuG 202 Lichtenstein BC*. The screens shown (L to R) a target at 1.3 km high and to the left; target at 2.1 km ahead, and ground echoes at a flying height of 3.7 km (*Fritz Trenkle*)

up to the full requirements and expectations for all-round surveillance. Especially useful was its ability to continue to operate with good results in the face of *Window* and other forms of jamming. Its data could be transmitted over many miles by another system called the *Landbriefträger* (Rural postman) where the traces from the screen were modulated on a carrier and sent over high-frequency coaxial cable, or by centimetric radio links such as *Michael*, to plotting stations a great distance away.

Experiments were also carried out on different forms of the *Jagdschloss*, one of which was the *Jagdschloss-Lang* designed to operate between 75 and 120 MHz, with 200 kW of power to an antenna array of 6 by 36 metres. But this was overshadowed by the *Jagdschloss-Umstellung* with even more power delivered to an antenna on a massive frame measuring 3 by 48 metres which had to be supported and rotated on an equally large circular track. And as if carried away by the excellent reports of these equipments, the Research Station at Werneuchen even considered the possibilities of using a *Wassermann L* to build the *Wassermann-Panorama* which, if the idea had ever come to fruition, would certainly have been the world's largest panoramic system.

During this time Telefunken had kept an eye on developments. They had their own ideas about panoramic systems, and were determined to come up with something which would put all the rest in the shade. But at first they had their hands full with a design called *Panorama-Kanada* which they were trying to get to work satisfactorily. This was actually based on a British radar captured at Tobruk, but as it was of a lower technical standard they abandoned the project in favour of one of their own designs known as the *Jagdwagen-Pantowiel*. This equipment, which appeared in a number of different forms, gave very good service and played a major part in future developments to be discussed later. Telefunken also found time during this period to experiment with a light mobile search radar called *Dinkelsbühl*. This was a combination of the *Euklid* system and a new design from their laboratories, but it never came to anything. A similar fate came to another idea called *Klein-Flukos* which was to have been used by the Observer Corps. The *Jagdwagen*, however, was their pièce de résistance.

In the meantime it was discovered that the beam from the *Jagdschloss* could pass unattenuated through wire netting, and apart from the advantages of camouflage it was also found that approaching aircraft could be located before the echo began to fade out. In the course of investigating this phenomenon it was realised that an even better result might ensue from simultaneous operation on two different frequencies. To this end they designed the *Jagdschloss-Michael* which employed the antennas of the *DMG 4K Michael* system attached to the ends of the *Jagdschloss* array, thus increasing the overall length to 54 metres. These antennas were excited by a *Würzburg* system whose transmissions were synchronised with those of the *Jagdschloss* so that both sets of results were displayed on the screen. This gave a range of 300 km, and the designers had hardly finished congratulating themselves when orders were received to cancel the project. No reason has ever been known for this apart from the prevailing war situation.

A similar end came to the *Jagdschloss MA*. This was similar in principle to the *Jagdschloss-Michael* and developed at the same time. It utilised a 150 kW *Würzburg* transmitter on 560 MHz with a 3 by 24 metre antenna from the *Michael*, thus making a system with only one frequency range but with very much improved beaming characteristics. Believing this could be bettered, Telefunken then designed a model called the *Jagdschloss MB* which they tested near Berlin. This delivered 150 kW on 560 MHz to an enormous antenna composed of 18 *Würzburg A* reflectors measuring 3 by 54 metres. The system proved very satisfactory but the war situation prevented the completion of the 12 models which were ordered. In fact, only one was delivered to the services and this had an even bigger array of two rows of 18 pairs of *Würzburg* reflectors mounted one above the other, but little more is now known about it.

In the meantime Siemens had been busy with a demand to provide foolproof recognition equipment for fighter guidance in combination with an acceptable search radar. For some time their laboratories had been working on a design which incorporated the IFF transmitter *Kuh* (Cow) on 110 to 125 MHz and its accompanying receiver *Gemse* (Chamois) on 143 to 158 MHz which was also furnished with a PPI screen. The system was called the *FuMG 405 Jagdhütte* (Hunting Lodge) and carried large rotating antennas, together with the IFF elements, on a 17 metre wide framework. Production of this model was delayed by the war situation until January 1945 and in any case only five models were delivered. But as far as it saw service it performed extremely well due to its design as a secondary radar system. Although full technical details are hard to come by it is known that it resisted jamming very well,

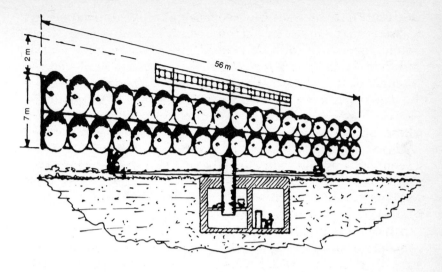

Figure 20 Artist's impression of the proposed *Jagdschloss MB* panoramic radar employing 36 *Würzburg* reflectors (*Fritz Trenkle*).

and was hardly affected by ground returns, this last benefit enabling it to be erected on mountain tops where the resulting increase in range was an additional bonus.

Lorenz, however, had an unhappy time during the development of what seemed to be a promising new system based on their *FuG 200 Hohentwiel* (30 kW, 560 MHz). The idea was that two segments of a paraboloid, for transmission and reception, were so arranged that the resulting beam would be much narrower than one from a single paraboloid. But an otherwise good start was sadly accompanied by an unfortunate and tragic accident in the laboratory in which a number of technicians were badly injured, and this put the development of the system back for several months, but the *Propeller*, as it was called, seemed destined for bad luck, for though it eventually passed into its second stage where it was known as the *Propeller H*, and with what was believed to be excellent direction-finding characteristics, no sooner had it been erected on a tower for testing when it burst into flames and was destroyed.

Telefunken were now employing the new PPI screen code-named *Drauf*. This was incorporated in a design which used their *FuSE 65 Würzburg Riese* and known as the *Riese P*. And although this had a rather poor resolution factor owing to the use of the relatively small 7 metre reflector, a large number of models were built and put into service. Later, this was re-designed to operate on 9 cm and went to the Navy as the *FuMO 15 Scheer*.

As the production of the *Jagdschloss* took longer than planned, a stop-gap was called for. Telefunken rose to the occasion and came up with an idea called the *Dreh-Freya* (Rotating Freya). This system used the latest *Freya LZ* from Lorenz which appeared in the summer of 1944, which had horizontally polarised broadband antennas for the frequencies between 120 and 158 MHz and a power of 30 kW. The resolution was improved by transposing the antennas, and a feature of the design was that it worked not only as a panoramic search radar, but as a standard direction-finding system as well. As a kind of split-system radar, complete with IFF, it was a novel departure from the usual range of equipment, and although it had a range of only about 50 km against aircraft 8 km high, it had the advantage of being easy to transport. As it happened, no orders were placed for it because a less expensive solution to the problem was found in another system called the *Panorama-Hohentwiel*, or *Pantowiel*, of which more later.

At this time Lorenz were fortunate in having the services of two able and dedicated researchers, Dr Messmer and Dr Schnabel, who refused to believe that the original *Propeller* system was a failure. Having convinced authority that it was worthwhile persevering with it, they re-designed it and called it the *Jagdhaus*. A few months later the first model was erected at Dergischow near Zeesen and went into action at the end of 1944. Like the higher-frequency version of the *Jagdschloss*, the *Jagdhaus* operated between 175 and 230 MHz with 300 kW of power, thus giving it a range of 300 km; the transmitter employed a pair of AS 1010 pulse triodes with the pulse system of the *FMG 40 Freya* over an oil-filled pulse-transformer at 20 kV, and the antenna was an interesting arrangement made from two transposed segments of a 10 by 11 metre paraboloid which delivered a beamwidth of 1°. Complete with an IFF system, the equipment was installed in the Berlin Zoo, and proved so successful that a further fifteen were immediately ordered. While further details of this equipment are now unobtainable, it is known that the installation at Dergischow fell into Russian hands in a virtually undamaged condition, and the personnel captured with it were ordered to make what repairs were necessary and raise the power to 750 kW. According to German sources this was one of the most valuable pieces of equipment ever captured by the Red Army.

The *Jagdwagen-Pantowiel* mentioned earlier was the inspiration of Dr Christ and Dr Gotthard Müller of Lorenz. Classified as the *FuMG 408 Jagdwagen-Pantowiel* it operated between 545 and 565 MHz with a power of 30 kW and used much of the equipment of the *FuG 200 Hohentwiel*. The new PPI screen *Type LB 9 Drauf* was also employed in conjunction with a new and very sensitive receiver, and the system was mounted on a *Kurmark* platform. The U-shaped rotating mast supported an antenna array consisting of 32 vertical dipoles set side by side. Three different models of this system were built and proved so successful that an accelerated production was ordered, but again the equipment fell into Russian hands at the end of the war.

At this time Telefunken also designed a long-range panoramic radar called *Europa* which was noted for its excellent height-finding, but apart from the fact that it was equipped with IFF technical details are no longer available. Similarly, very little is now known about the *Wellenreiter* (Wave rider) designed by the Ernst Orlich Institut in Danzig, except that it employed a 'long dash' continuous-wave transmitter and depended on the natural resonance of the target aircraft for its performance.

The last centimetric panoramic radar from Telefunken before the end of the war was the *Forsthaus K*. This was something of an engineering colossus because it employed a cylindrical antenna 48 metres long and 7.7 metres high, supported on an iron circular track and rotated by a *Leonard* mechanism at 3½ rpm. The paraboloid contained three synchronously pulsed transmitters and three receivers which were adapted from the *Euklid* system. This new equipment operated on 1,100 MHz with 100 kW. Height finding was achieved through the selection of one to three height ranges as displayed on the screen. The IFF antennas used created problems at first due to interaction with the radar antennas proper, mainly because the radar beams were generated diagonally to the axes of their antennas, but these troubles were finally overcome by siting the IFF antennas diagonally to the paraboloid.

Despite production difficulties twelve of these equipments were erected near Merseburg in the Eifel region, but were destroyed by Allied fighter-bombers before they could go into full service. It is known that at least four variations of this radar were ordered, one of them being a model of reduced size known as the *Forsthaus FK* which was fitted with a smaller paraboloid of 3 by 24 metres and used only two transmitters and receivers from the *Euklid* system, the entire equipment being mounted on a *Jagdschloss* platform.

A combination of the Flak radar *FuMG Kulmbach* and equipment from the 9 cm *Berlin* (discussed later) was the basis of the *Forsthaus Z*. This also used three slotted radiators in a cylindrical paraboloid of 2.5 by 24 metres, but with only one transmitter on 3,300 MHz with 100 kW of power. Three receivers were used as before, and the entire equipment was again built on the *Jagdschloss* platform. A 3 cm version of this, to be known as the *Forsthaus X*, was also planned, but further details are no longer obtainable.

As has been mentioned, the long-distance transmission of data was carried out over a system called the *Landbriefträger*, and the versatility of this was such that it calls for more detail. Not only the revolutions of the antenna, but the pulse-rate-frequency up to 300 kHz with the accompanying returns, could be carrier-modulated and fed over coaxial cable from distances as far away as Tremmen and Werneuchen to the Flak bunker in the Berlin Zoo. Here the signals were demodulated and fed to the display screens.

A system for the transmission of data to the *Seeburg Tisch* (discussed later) was also used on similar lines. Produced by Siemens, it comprised a transmitter and receiver, narrow-beam light projectors for the *Seeburg Tisch*, and an electronic calculator, the latter being made by the Askania Company. This method of transmission was known as the *Luxor* and gave very good results.

A more complicated system was designed by Dr Bialk at Telefunken in co-operation with the Zeiss Company and known as *Haselnuss* (Hazelnut). With this, the data could either be fed to a special plotting screen on which map representations measuring 10 by 100 cm were displayed, and which also included an electronic calculator, or it could be fed over a long-distance transmission system whereby the map co-ordinates corresponded to different voltages from capacitors which generated a tone frequency variation of about 20 Hz around a central frequency of 700 Hz. Eight transmission channels could be sent successively to a single display screen.

Other data-transmission systems of this time were designed by Siemens and included the *Komando-Anlage GT* (Command Installation), the *Neue-Fluko Technik* (New Fluko Technique), the *Klotzscher Tisch* (Klotzscher Table), and the *Fuchs* (Fox), the latter being used for the long-distance transmission of data from two positions to the central control station. It is known that similar equipments were manufactured at this time, but very little is known about them apart from the names. These include the *Fernzeichen-Anlage* (Long Distance Character Installation) maker unknown, the *Verbesserte-Lichtpunktwerfer* (Improved Light-Point Projection) by the Fitze Company, and the *Gefechtsbildschreiber* (Battle Scene Writer) by the Möller Company.

CHAPTER SEVEN

Airborne Radar

The earliest experiments into airborne radar took place long before the war in the form of radio altimeters, Runge's *Lichtenstein A* being predominant. But the systematic development of airborne radar began in early 1940 only after the High Command enquired of firms and research institutes as to whether such systems were practicable at this time.

For this reason many early experimental models were developed by as many different firms due to the common interest in pulse-measuring techniques in those days, but a delay of several months took place before any of these equipments could be seriously considered because most of them were far too heavy and bulky for the limited space in an aircraft, to say nothing of the disposable load reserves.

The biggest obstacle was, however, the insistence of the Luftwaffe that all antennas were to be installed within the aircraft so that the aerodynamic surface would not be affected and the aircraft's range subsequently shortened. And a further point to remember is that while the ground presents a very large surface for both radio-altimeter and radar techniques, an aircraft or ship, by comparison, provides only a very small return, and to obtain useful ranges the transmitter power, receiver sensitivity, and the antenna efficiency must be correspondingly intensified. In any event, it was not until February 1941 that external antennas were permitted to be fitted to aircraft.

It should also be explained at this point that while this chapter deals with the development of airborne radar, many of the systems mentioned were adopted and adapted for other purposes according to the prevailing demands of the war. Like many other devices, an equipment expressly designed for one particular purpose very often worked as well if not better for another.

The first problems to be tackled were those of greater power and the better focusing of the antenna beam, and it is interesting to learn that the Radar Research Regiment at Köthen had the novel and enterprising idea of building a *Würzburg A* in a Fw200.

They actually went ahead and flight tested it, but for some reason no records exist of the results. It is believed that it had a similar fate to the one that attended a venture by Kühnhold's Naval Communications Establishment when they used parts of the *Freya* for a nightfighter radar they called *Wendelstein*. A literal translation of this name is 'spiral stone', and they actually built twenty of these sytems using *Freya* dipoles physically shortened by the use of base loading coils, and on 125 MHz with 8 kW of power. Owing to its large bulk, the system could only be installed in a Do217 and it may come as no surprise to learn that it promptly lived up to its name when the aircraft crashed shortly after take-off. (Much to the concern of the Swiss in whose territory it fell.)

At the beginning of July 1941 a research model ASV radar was built by Atlas-Werke of Munich and installed in a Fw200 of KG40. Known as the *Atlas*, it worked on a frequency of 136 MHz (power unknown) and was built with very small unit construction. A display unit was provided in the radio operator's space, with a repeater situated near the pilot. A simple dipole transmitting antenna was mounted on a tripod below the cockpit, and the receiving antennas were quarter-wave stubs fixed to left and right below the fuselage. The display unit consisted of a 4 cm screen on which vertical traces were shown against a horizontal timebase line. But while little is now known about this particular model, it is thought that it saw very little employment.

At about the same time a British Mark I ASV radar fell into German hands and their scientists lost no time in evaluating it. For this purpose it was rebuilt in a Fw200 and flown over the Atlantic to find out how it responded to German jamming, and much to the satisfaction of the technicians it was found very susceptible to such countermeasures. As already mentioned, the Germans could never understand why the British built such cumbersome equipments. The screen of the *Mark I*, for example, was over 10 inches in diameter, and the large accumulation of components over an equally large chassis gave rise to their expression *viel Luft in den Geräten*,[1] an idiom for wasted space.

At the end of 1941 a few models of a new system called the ASV (Air to Surface Vessel) *Neptun S* were tested in Condors over Norway but gave ranges of only 15 km against ships. A few weeks later, in early 1942, Gema developed the *Rostock* (no classification) on 120 MHz, and despite the problem of a very small power supply, managed to raise a pulse power of 1.5 kW which gave ranges up to 30 km. The receiver and display unit were constructed as a self-contained item, but though the designers had struggled to make it as small as possible, it was still too large to use except in a very big aircraft. The transmitting antennas were two horizontal dipoles and reflectors mounted on the nose, and two similar arrays were attached to the wings and canted outwards for reception. Bearings were determined by the use of an alternating capacity switch which coupled the receiver to each wing antenna in turn (A/N bearings) and the resulting echoes were shown on the screen as traces to the left and right of the vertical time-base line, the latter being adjustable to cover selected parts of a 60 km range, while the range itself was shown by vertical traces against calibrated engraved marks.

This model was successfully tested in November 1942 at Werneuchen when it was installed in He111s and Fw200s employed expressly for these purposes. By April 1943 the system was installed in fifteen reconnaissance Fw200s for Atlantic missions.

It was also decided at this time to have another look at the *Atlas*. The engineers made use of horizontal dipole whips in a configuration known as *Antler Antennas* which were fixed to the front and sides of the fuselage, and the 4 cm display screens were fitted with lenses for better viewing. (German engineers had a tendency to take miniaturisation too far at times.) The display system worked in the same way as the earlier model, except that now the receiver amplification had been so improved that stronger echoes no longer tended to swamp the screen. Whether this made direction-finding more accurate is doubtful, and in any case, like its predecessor, its weight was only suitable for large aircraft.

Also in November Werneuchen tested an ASV radar built by Gema to the specifications of the Naval Communications Establishment. This model rejoiced under the name *Prof*

---

[1] A lot of air in the apparatus.

Scherzer (Prof Joker) and had a search angle of 300° and a range of 80 km. A peculiarity of the system was that as the forward and side areas could be swept separately, two receivers were employed each with its own display unit of sweep screens. The antenna arrangement consisted of 18 retractable vertical whips, those for the transmitter being a pair of vertical quarter waves mounted in such a way as to provide an angle of 100° to the flight path. The first receiver was alternately switched to a group of four antennas under each wing tip, which swept right, left, and forward; while the second receiver was similarly connected to four antennas under the fuselage which covered the area diagonally to the left and right, but had only about one third of the range of the forward antennas. Tests with this system were, however, discontinued because its range, height and bearing accuracies were too poor, and its weight of 120 kg, as opposed to the 20 kg of the *Rostock*, was far too heavy.

After the crash of the *Wendelstein* model, a meeting was held on 11 April 1943 to discuss the matter, and the awkwardness of the antennas was held to be responsible. Few details of this meeting are available, but it is known that another antenna system was discussed and an attempt made to use it. From such details as can be seen from the only photograph of this system, it seems that a Ju88 was fitted with six half wave dipoles commonly fed from a vertically supported feedpoint as a transmitting array, with two similarly constructed antennas to the left and right of the fuselage, connected between the wings and tailplane. It is believed that a certain degree of reasonable direction-finding could be achieved to the sides and above, but little could be done about the front, rear, or below, unless additional antennas were attached. In any case, further development of the *Wendelstein* was stopped in the autumn of 1943.

As has been mentioned, Dr Christ and Dr Gotthard Müller of Lorenz began the development of the ASV radar *FuG 200 Hohentwiel* which, being based on the *FMG 40 Kurmark*, had a degree of maturity to begin with. It worked on 550 MHz, but the original power of 30 kW had to be reduced owing to problems of ionisation arcing caused by the greater flying heights then being achieved. The employment of these higher frequencies, however, permitted the use of much smaller antennas which, in this case, were eight pairs of dipoles and reflectors which produced a sharper beam and gave ranges of up to 80 km against ships and about 100 km for coastlines. The first model appeared in September 1942 and had only one set of antennas for transmitting and receiving mounted on the nose and accurately aligned to the flightpath, maximum direction-finding being displayed on the screen to one side of the timebase line. Following successful testing at Werneuchen A/N bearings were introduced, whereupon the accuracy for forward targets was somewhat reduced, but bearing accuracy, especially with approaching bombers, was improved to ± 1°. This version of the *Hohentwiel* entered service in August 1943 when it was installed in a number of reconnaissance aircraft such as the BV138, the BV222, the Fw200, the He177, and the Ju290.

To increase the search angle from about 110° to almost 300°, the BV222 was fitted with a pair of transmitting antennas and two parallel-switched receiving antennas, with an additional display screen, thus increasing the total number of antennas to nine standard arrays. For comparison direction-finding and target-approach, course alterations were made according to the signals from the forward antennas, and the screens were adjustable for ranges between 0 to 10 km and 0 to 100 km, though this was later changed to 0 to 15 km and 0 to 150 km. The range scale was etched on the glass of the screen, and the flying height could be established by using the echoes from the sea, as could the target's range. On close approach, the correct bearing angle was found by a combination of the radar and an optical system. For bombing operations the system was employed in conjunction with an extremely accurate mechanical calculator known as an *X-Uhr* (X-Clock), which gave the correct aiming point for the bombs.

The power amplifier stage used a pair of RD 12 TF pulse triodes in push-pull, and the pulse system used the thyratron S 1/132 from Telefunken and a modulation transformer with a breakdown current of 850 amps. The circuitry of the pulse system was considered to be so secret that although it was also used in other radars, such as *Neptun* and *Weilheim*, these were equipped with it only towards the end of the war. The receiver was a double superhet of very high sensitivity and was equipped with an 'artificial target' which enabled receiver tuning and range-measurement calibration to be carried out without being troubled by ground returns. This device was a crystal cemented to a glass bar which, on stimulation by the direct transmitter pulse, generated ultrasonic oscillations which were repeatedly reflected to the end of the bar before becoming damped by the arrival of a range-function tone, these reflected signals appearing at the timebase of the display

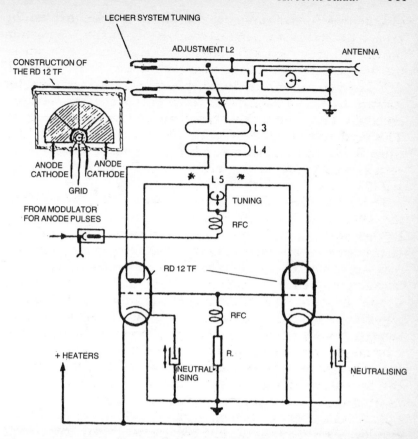

Figure 21 Circuit of the *Hohentweil* power amplifier stage and antenna coupling (*Fritz Trenkle*).

screen at intervals corresponding to 3 km, according to the sensitivity of the receiver.

Hohentwiel radars were installed in over 500 aircraft, though its later Marks were actually fitted in twice this number. Towards the end of the war a version called the *Hohentwiel II* was developed with simultaneous operation of the transmitter and receiver in synchronous tuning between 525 and 575 MHz. By now the earlier problems associated with the high power had been overcome, and it used a 40 kW transmitter of very compact design which, with improved receiver sensitivity, provided a close resolution of 150 metres. Further Marks of the model were the *Hohentwiel-Lang* on 110 to 160 MHz (used with the *EGON B* system) and the *Hohenstein* on 8.7 and 9.8 cm, both of which were still being produced at the end of the war. A plan was devised to include the *Hohentwiel* with the *FuG 212 Lichtenstein C 1* (described later), in order to increase the range of the latter. In fact, the range of the *Lichtenstein* was almost trebled by this inclusion, but as the additional antennas of the *Hohentwiel* introduced a further loss of speed the idea was abandoned.

In 1940, the *Flugfunkforschungsinstitut* (FFO) or Airborne Radio Research Institute under Dr H. Heine and Dr P. Maurer had begun to develop the *Neptun*. This had an initial power of 1.5 kW and a receiver with much improved sensitivity, and at the same time a new antenna arrangement was designed which employed Yagi antennas on the nose and whip antennas on the wings and fuselage which could either be switched from left to right or rotated around 90° above and below.

A different version of this arrangement was tested in early 1941 when a Ju52 was fitted with a crossed array of vertical antennas, each antenna having a driven element and two directors, but also a pair of reflectors set at an angle which were alternately switched to cover a wider area. At first, this idea seemed promising and Martini gave orders for it to be followed up, but after test flights had been made it was seen that the best range was only 15 km, and apart from the fact that the frequency was 182 MHz very few details are now forthcoming.

The British, who had carried out experiments with airborne radar before the war and had made headway with their equipment ever since, now had much better systems, and these were being used with success against German bombers over England. As a result of the increasing efficiency of the British radars an order was made in early 1942 for the development of rear-warning equipment for German bombers, and at the same time the question was raised as to the practicability of a forward-facing nightfighter radar with facilities for sweeping to left, right, above and below. The *Neptun* system seemed ideally suited to the former requirement and to this end the *FuG 216 Neptun R* was developed. This operated on 167 MHz with a power of 1.2 kW. The original vertical antennas were now attached to the undersides of the wings and angled at 180° to the rear, while a strut arrangement on the front of the wings carried horizontal Yagis with a reflector and two directors.

This was tested at Werneuchen in September 1942 and met with approval. About a dozen hand-made sets were then assembled and an order was placed with the Seibt Company for a further 100. These were principally used in single aircraft on bombing missions over England and could indicate the presence of enemy nightfighters up to 3.5 km, but if the enemy employed his IFF system many times this range could be attained, the range-scale of the display screen being adjustable from 2 to 10 km. The timebase line was displayed horizontally, with bright points to indicate every 2 km, and the reading of the target range was made from dark points within these areas. The enemy's position, that is left, right, above or below, was made obvious by its movements.

In June 1943, renewed research into the system was undertaken at Gotenhafen for the detection of sea targets, and from the tests conducted there the ASV radar *Neptun S (S2)* was developed. Horizontal dipoles were attached to both sides of the tail unit of a Fw200, with a reflector and two directors. Towards the front of the wings, easily angled outwards, were a pair of dipoles and reflectors for reception. With a more powerful transmitter delivering 2 kW from a pair of LV 13 pulse triodes in push-pull the range was about 25 km against ships and approximately 8 km for submarines. This system having proved successful, Seibt then received orders from the FFO for the development of another model to be called the rear-warning radar *FuG 217 Neptun R 2*. This differed from its predecessors in having a new 2 kW transmitter and a new receiver, both of which could be tuned to pre-set frequencies between 158 and 178 MHz while in flight. This equipment proved most successful and was employed in bombers until the middle of 1944, when it was converted for use in nightfighters, the horizontal dipoles being replaced with vertical whips.

In that year Siemens also developed a lightweight nightfighter radar for single-seater aircraft. Based on the original *Neptun* it used two horizontal dipoles and reflectors on the wings, the left hand arrangement being used for bearings and the right hand for height. To assist in determining bearings these height-finding antennas were arranged parallel to the transmitting antennas, which were of similar size and number and fitted one above the other with indirect coupling. The right and left hand antennas were alternately fed to the receiver over a motorised rotary switch to give A/N bearings, and the receiver output was similarly switched to the display screen. This system provided a much better beaming pattern with a corresponding longer range. For height-finding a reversal method was employed by the parallel switching of the left hand dipoles to change them to transmitting antennas and the right hand ones for reception. Two screens were employed in the display unit, one for bearings where the traces were shown horizontally from left to right across a calibrated scale which could be adjusted between 10 and 100 km, and a similar screen for height-finding displayed traces of echoes from above or below, but gave no range. The equipment had a normal range in any case of between 3 and 5 km, but when it picked up an enemy IFF transmission it was dramatically increased to 70 km. Unfortunately, the system found little favour with the aircrew because two screens had to be observed, and besides, the antennas reduced speed and hindered vision.

Within a short time an improved version was produced and given the classification *FuG 217 J Neptun 2J* (later known as the *FuG 217 J 1 Neptun J 1*). This was installed in small numbers in the Fw190 and, it is believed, also in the Bf109, the transmitting antennas being whips mounted on the nose just in front of the cockpit. Vertical whips were also used for bearings and fitted on the wings, while similar antennas were fixed beneath the fuselage for direction-finding. The display unit was much smaller as it contained only one screen which was built into the instrument panel in front of the pilot. As before, both left and right receiving antennas were fed over an alternating switch to the receiver and finally to the left and right deflection plates of the tube, and for height-finding the antennas under the fuselage were actuated by a push button, the resulting echoes being shown on the upper half of the screen as traces above or below a horizontal timebase line. It is thought that similar equipments under the designation of *FuG 217 JR Neptun* (with an additional rearward antenna system) were fitted into some aircraft, but there is no confirmation of this.

With the advent of the Me262 jet fighter and its corrresponding higher speed, the pilot was fully occupied with his approach and manoeuvring; and as his weapons were now of larger calibre with a lower rate of fire he had only about three seconds from locating his target in which to do everything. To meet this problem the FFO ordered the development of a system in which one of the transmitted pulses was fed over a phase-converter to the 3 km scale marks of a *Neptun* radar in a delayed sequence, and at the appearance of a target echo the delayed pulse from the echo was fed over another delayed-running system until a previously determined range, say, 1.5 km, was reached. Such a system was designed by Siemens and called the *EG 3 Elfe 3*. This was intended for use in conjunction with the day-fighter system *FuG 217 RV Neptun*, itself another version of the *FuG 217 R Neptun* but with forward-facing antennas for range measurement. Bearings and height-finding were not required as the pilot was expected to find the target by eye in his closing approach.

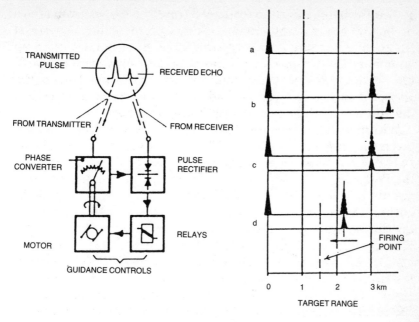

Figure 22 Diagram of the automatic firing system *Elfe 3* (*Fritz Trenkle*).

During a demonstration of this system arranged by General Adolf Galland at Christmas 1944, Göring (who usually had an aversion to radio or radar aids) was so impressed that he declared it to be the *Panzerfaust der Luftwaffe*[1] (anti-tank weapon of the Luftwaffe). But whether the system was fitted in day or night fighters is not known, and in any case it had only a short life because the production line fell victim to Allied bombing.

An interesting system developed near the end of the war was the *FuG 217 J2 Neptun II J2*. This could use either the antennas of the *Neptun J1* or the Yagis of the *FuG 218 V I* which will be discussed later. This was somewhat similar to the *Hohentwiel* as far as the transmitter was concerned but employed a newly designed pulse method using only three valves instead of nine: one thyratron and two power amplifiers. The EHT (Extra High Tension) for the tube was generated over a resistance-capacity network from the transmitter supply and the traces were observed through an engraved glass cover. Ranges were displayed as traces at right angles on a diagonal timebase line which appeared from the bottom left of the screen and finished at the top right, while those for bearings (from the left and

---

[1] The *Panzerfaust* was a disposable one-man single-shot anti-tank rocket launcher throwing a hollow-charge head of great penetrative power. Its main drawbacks were its short range and the give-away flame from the rocket tube.

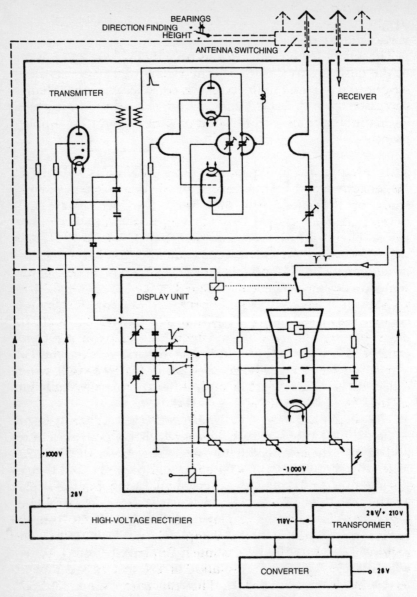

Figure 23 Layout of the simplified *Neptun-Liliput* (*Fritz Trenkle*).

right antennas respectively) were indicated by the initials *L* and *R* (*Links-Rechts*) engraved on the glass and illuminated by a trace in the form of a blob of light. Height was shown in a similar manner by the letters *H* and *T* (*Hoch-Tief*) at the top and bottom. This display unit was considerably smaller than that of the earlier *Neptun J1*, and in fact new forms of screen display had been the subject of research for some time. Much interest was shown in one where the simultaneous indications of range, height and bearings were displayed on diagonal, horizontal and vertical lines respectively.

There is little doubt that for its time the *Neptun II J2* was one of the most sophisticated airborne radars of its type. Its all-up weight (not to mention the cost) was considerably lower than its successor the *FuG 218 R Neptun*. And as a result of dispersing its manufacture over the country 50 sets could be supplied monthly.

The development of *Neptun* had not gone unnoticed by Dr H. Hagenhaus and Dr H. Brandau of Siemens. After a careful study of the equipment they were convinced they could develop an even smaller rear-warning radar at an even lower price. Their contribution was the *FuG 217 L Neptun-Liliput* which operated on only one frequency. But before serious development of this project could begin they were commissioned to design a system for ranges between 163 and 167 MHz with six channels which could be selected as desired in flight to combat enemy jamming. Provision also had to be made for incorporating the new IFF system *FuG 226 Neuling* (Newcomer). It is interesting to note that the first version, the *FuG 218 R Neptun III R*, also included an infra-red search system called the *FuG 280 Kiel Z*, and although this was built into nightfighters its operational success is unknown.

The preparatory work on the *Neptun III R* had hardly begun when the designers had better ideas which led to an even faster and more efficient production of its successor, the *FuG 218 Neptun III V1*. This was also used in nightfighters, and though the antenna arrangement was very similar to that of the *Neptun J1*, they were now alternately switched to beam rearwards. Only slight differences in the display unit distinguished it from the earlier model, and it had a completely new transmitter and receiver, the latter having a much improved muting system which resulted in a close resolution of 120 metres as compared to the 200 metrres of the *J1*. The transmitter power of 2 kW gave a range of about 5 km, and a similar antenna arrangement to that of the *J2* was used whereby both left and right arrays were connected over a rotary switching system, except that now two dipoles were used simultaneously for bearings and height. The others remained unused although plans had been put forward for their employment as rear-warning elements.

On twin-engined aircraft the four forward-facing antennas used vertical polarisation and were mounted on the nose in a square configuration. Of these, two were parallel switched and directly fed, while the remaining pair, also parallel switched, were fed over a rotary phase-conversion system so that the whole array could be used for simultaneous transmission and reception. For rear-warning purposes a single horizontal driven element and reflector were mounted on the tail unit. At first the system included two screens for forward-searching and rear-warning but these were later replaced by a simplified equipment known as the *Einheits-Sichtgerätes* (Standard Display Unit) with selectable range and direction-finding controls. This however did not go into production because the aircrew preferred the normal unit which had no additional controls, and was in any case much easier to use because warnings were also audible by ear. Before 1 April 1945 a number of Me262 B-1 jets had been fitted with the system since the new screens and rear-warning antennas were appropriate for the speed, and especially as the passive-warning system *FuG 350 Z* (discussed later) was also installed. Also at this time a different method of antenna construction, including broadband arrays, was tested by Rechlin in a Me262 (V 056) and these, together with the IFF system *FuG 226* (discussed later) with antennas mounted on the left wing, were employed just before the end of the war.

At about this time (mid 1944) Siemens designed a very effective radiator called the *Kanzel-Ring* (Cockpit ring) antenna. This was made from four metal foil dipoles and reflectors built into a radome, and at the same time they developed the *Morgenstern* (Morning star) antenna which will be discussed later.

These systems were designed primarily for the *Neptun* series, of which over 150 models of the *FuG 218* version were installed up to the end of the war. In February 1945 a nightfighter version of the Do335 B carried the latest model, the *FuG 218 G Neptun III G*, which employed a 20 kW transmitter code-named *Gustav* with the antennas of the *Neptun V1* model. The last of this series however was a design by Siemens called the *FuG 219a Weilheim a* with a 100 kW transmitter, and for this they had developed a new valve known as the *LS 81 Hantel* (Dumb-bell). This was a massive affair with a 30 cm heavy pressure steel envelope, but its employment, together with the planned *FuG 219b Weilheim b*, was stopped by the deteriorating war situation.

By far the greatest contribution to airborne radar came from the teams headed by Dr Runge, Muth, Urtel, Brand and Ilberg at Telefunken. Runge's *Lichtenstein A* was modified and tested with forward facing antennas on a He111, and indeed showed some promise as mentioned. But the prohibition on the use of external antennas was a bad mistake on the part of the Luftwaffe High Command. In fact, the antipathy of some of the hierarchy to radar in aircraft was a serious set-back to their cause. Dr Herbert Kümmritz, a Telefunken scientist and former Luftwaffe officer, speaks with experience of those times:

> The attitude of leading German politicians and military personnel to technical matters during World War II ... believe me, that was a disaster. Not only the leading military men, but also pilots and navigators, were unable to recognise the significance of modern electronic assistance. For example, the introduction of *Lichtenstein* was delayed for a whole year, from 1941 to 1942, because the pilots refused to fly with an antenna outside the body of the aircraft. In their eyes the 'mattress' as they called it interfered with the speed and mobility of the plane and had no real advantage. In 1942 they had no option but to fly with it, but they showed great resistance to it all the same. In many cases they took a hacksaw and removed the antennas.
>
> In fact, it was not until 1944 that most pilots began to appreciate the value of radar in aircraft. And the reason for their objection was that the German Air Force was run by men of the First World War who did not appreciate the fact that in the twenty years between 1918 and 1938 great progress had been made in scientific techniques. They began where they ended in 1918. In their view aircraft were meant to be flown just as they flew their biplanes in those early days.[1]

In fairness to the rank and file of the Luftwaffe it should be explained that Kümmritz's remarks really applied to the more senior members of the service who, as in any military body, were naturally inclined to keep one eye on the leadership. Their attitude to radar and other electronic aids was often ambivalent because of Göring's love-hate relationship with the new technology. At one moment he would be full of praise and enthusiasm for a new technical gadget – at another, he would denounce it. On being present at a demonstration of the *Würzburg A* in the early days, he made his celebrated announcement that the Ruhr would never be bombed; and on

---

[1] Kümmritz. Letter to the author.

another occasion when Martini demonstrated a radionavigatio-
nal aid, he declared, 'Radio aids contain boxes with coils, and I
do not like boxes with coils.' On learning of radar screens in
cockpits he commented scathingly about 'unnecessary cinema
shows for pilots.' Small wonder that his followers did not know
at times which way to turn. And when Udet, who had shown
scorn for Runge's *Darmstadt*, actually led a group of
radar-guided fighters on a defensive patrol, they were even
more nonplussed.

Faced with this peculiar state of affairs the industry could do
no more than shrug its shoulders and carry on. Telefunken in
particular, having brought as much pressure as possible on an
unbending Luftwaffe Command in respect of external
antennas, went ahead and designed an internal array called the
Sägefisch (Sawfish). Although exhaustive tests were carried out
with this for nearly a year, it gave only poor results. Clearly,
internal antennas were useless for the type of equipment then
in use, and Runge, being a forceful personality and accustomed
to having his own way, went to Martini and told him so. Martini
of course knew the limitations of these antennas as much as
Runge did, and taking the bit between his teeth, took the
matter to higher level. What actually passed at this meeting is

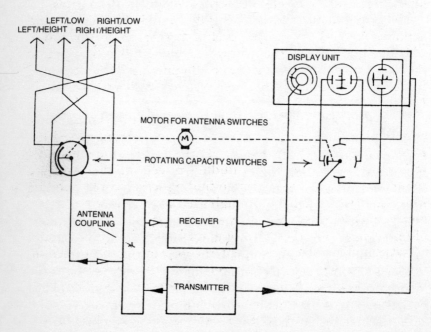

Figure 24 Simplified layout of the *FuG 202 Lichtenstein BC* and the FuG 212
Lichtenstein C1 (Fritz Trenkle).

not known, except that in autumn 1941 the High Command gave in and permitted external antennas to be used.

Telefunken then went ahead and designed the *FuG 202 Lichtenstein BC* which worked on 490 MHz with 1.5 kW of pulse power, with a very sensitive superregenerative receiver with 6 stages of amplification. The antennas were 4 dipoles and reflectors mounted on the nose of the aircraft in a square arrangement, and these were employed for simultaneous transmission and reception over a motor-driven capacity switch to transmitter or receiver. Transmitting power was generated and fed via phase-conversion through the switch to give a narrow elongated cone-shaped lobe symmetrical to the body of the aircraft. For reception the antennas were connected with a *Quirl* arrangement in such a way that they fed the left and right deflection plates of the bearing-finding screen and the top and bottom plates of the height-finding screen, thus providing a synchronous display according to the rotation of the antenna pattern. The display unit had in fact three screens; one of which showed all targets within range of 8 km, while the pair for height and bearings had vertical and horizontal timebase lines respectively on which the echoes were displayed in 'back to back' fashion. These screens only indicated about 1.5 km of the total range which was selected by phase-conversion controls.

The equipment was successfully tested in August and September 1941 by Oberleutnant Becker in a Do215B-5, who had the luck to shoot down six enemy bombers before the set broke down. But after eliminating these teething troubles Telefunken put the system into production in February 1942.

In November 1942 components from this system were employed in a new equipment for torpedo aiming called the *FuG 202 T Lichtenstein BC/T*. Two of the antennas were removed, as was the height-finding screen, and a revolving circle was displayed on the range-finding screen corresponding with the aiming point, but though the range accuracy of $\pm$ 100 metres and the close resolution were very good, the total range of only 6.5 km was thought not good enough. A great amount of time and trouble was spent on improving the direction-finding accuracy but it was never better than 2.5° due to the wide search-angle. After a great deal of testing in a He111 at Werneuchen the idea was abandoned.

At the same time Rechlin had been engaged in the development of a new type of cannon fire system in which the guns were mounted in an upwards-firing position. This was

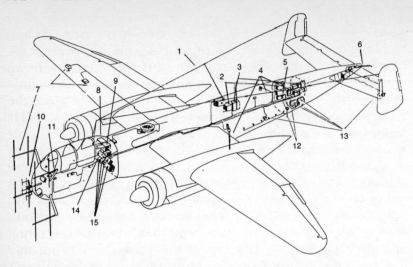

1. Fixed antenna for *FuG 10 P* radio telephony
2. Equipment of *FuG 212 Lichtenstein C1*
3. Equipment of *FuG 220 Lichtenstein SN 2*
4. *FuG 16 ZY* IFF equipment
5. *FuG 10 P* R/T equipment
6. *FuG 10 P* auxiliary trailing antenna
7. Antenna for *FuG 220 Lichtenstein SN 2*
8. *FuG 212 Lichtenstein C1* display unit
9. *FuG 220 Lichtenstein SN 2* display unit
10. Antenna for *FuG 212 Lichtenstein C1*

11. Navigational instruments
12. *FuG 25a Erstling*
13. *FuBL 2 F* Blind Landing Equipment
14. *FuG 16 ZY* IFF Display Unit
15. *FuG 10 P* Instruments

Figure 25 He 219 nightfighter showing the layout of the radar and radio-navigational aids (*Fritz Trenkle*).

known as the *Schräge Musik* system[1] (Hot Music) and was first tested in a Do17Z-10 equipped with a combined radar installation built from the *Lichtenstein BC* and the *FuG 202 0 Lichtenstein 0* (described later). Although the idea showed some promise the results were not as good as had been expected and the development was therefore put aside for a year. At the end of this time it was revived with some success.

During this period Telefunken came up with an idea for using the *Lichtenstein BC* with a different kind of antenna system for locating low-flying aircraft. These antennas were fixed beneath the fuselage of a He111 and a gyroscope was built in to make a horizontal rotary system whereby the bearings and horizontal direction of targets could be found.

---

[1] *Schräge Musik* is correctly translated as 'Oblique Music'. The term is apt, not only because the guns were mounted for upward firing, but also because it was a slang expression for jazz, prohibited by Hitler but secretly listened to and enjoyed by many, especially the Luftwaffe crews.

This was known as the *FuG 202 U Lichtenstein U* and gave very good results; but as at this time the British resorted to blind bombing at heights above the cloud base, the adjustments for height and speed became more difficult than with an arrangement of upper antennas and the idea was reluctantly abandoned. A similar end came to another project in which the *Lichtenstein BC* was modified to work on 260 and 333 MHz instead of its normal 490 MHz. This was the *FuG 214 Lichtenstein BC/R* in which only the range-finding screen was used, the others being covered up. Three research models were actually tried out, but the ranges were rather poor; Rechlin was not in favour with the idea because continuous operation and observation was needed, and the circular timebase presentation used in the system was harder to read than a normal horizontal line. Perhaps of some interest is the fact that this was the only Telefunken system that employed whip antennas with left and right attachments below the wings, rather on the lines of the *Neptun R*.

Nothing daunted, Dr Muth and Dr Urtel pressed on and came up with the *FuG 212 Lichtenstein C1*. Its circuitry and mode of operation was very similar to its forerunner, the *BC1*, and used the same frequency of 490 MHz with the same antenna system. But the transmitter, receiver and display unit, together with the antenna switching, were completely new. Great things were expected of this model, but after Werneuchen tested it in a Do17 Z-10 in May 1942 the looked-for improvements in range and acquisition angle were not forthcoming. Nevertheless, as nothing better was available at the time, orders were placed for a large series to be produced. This decision had been taken after testing a following model called the *FuG 212/1 Lichtenstein C1S*, of which even greater things had been expected, and which it was hoped would furnish a much better acquisition-angle by the use of larger antennas, but it defeated all these expectations by merely introducing a colossal loss of speed. By the autumn of 1943 research had also been carried out into the making of a broadband antenna system which involved the use of a streamlined design of four vertical dipoles. Known as the *FuG 212a Lichtenstein W* this had a larger acquisition angle but the range was rather poor at only about 2 km.

By now Telefunken were getting annoyed at systems that seemed promising at first but proved poor in practice. Determined to put the matter right, they concentrated on the good resolution of the *Lichtenstein C* model and the wide-angle antennas of the *BC* system and combined them experimentally with the wide-search system of the new *Lichtenstein SN 2* (described later). This resulted in a rather unexpected poor close resolution but a good range, and as this was the best that could be done at the time they were obliged to continue with the development. The original three screens were replaced by a smaller display unit called the *SG 212a* which contained two screens for bearings and height, with selectable ranges of between 4 and 10 km which were read as 'cross-fadable' points on the calibration scale.

Another equipment in this series was the *FuG 212/2 Lichtenstein C2* which operated in the *Wismar* range of selectable frequencies between 420 and 480 MHz. It is ironic that this equipment gave quite good results but could only be used very infrequently because the range was jammed by the enemy, a circumstance all the more unwelcomed by Telefunken's design staff since they had designed a very efficient superhet to replace the older superregenerative receiver. Its successors, the *Lichtenstein C2/B* and *Lichtenstein E*, were combined to give ranges up to 12 km, and this system also employed the automatic firing system *Lichtenstein-Pauke* (Lichtenstein Drum). It is believed that this system was the forerunner of the *FuG 215 Pauke A* nightfighter blind-firing method which worked between 410 and 490 MHz with a pulse power of 30 kW in conjunction with the now much improved firing system *Schräge Musik*. As this equipment used a much smaller antenna array it was decided to enclose it in a streamline wooden casing on the nose, but as this produced some curious antenna patterns experiments were conducted with a parabolic reflector 70 cm in diameter and a rotating dipole which were enclosed in the same housing and gave better results. A twin screen display unit was installed and though the total range was only 1.5 km the range accuracy was considered good at 5 metres.

In 1942 Dr Muth had begun the development of the ASV radar *FuG 213 Lichtenstein S*. Originally operating on 72 MHz, but later changed to 91 MHz, it soon progressed to a line of laboratory models that required very little construction space. A common suspension frame contained the transmitter and a superhet receiver, and the display unit was again a twin screen design having a circular timebase scale showing ranges between 0 and 60 km and a bearing screen with phase-conversion selection. Left and right antennas were mounted on the front of the wings and switched electronically as before. It came into operational use in 1943 but only a few models were installed as the range against ships was only about 60 km and the close resolution of between 300 and 500 metres was considered very poor. In view of this an attempt was made to improve matters by combining the bearing accuracy of the *Lichtenstein S* with the range-finding of the *C1*, the combination being known as the *FuG 212/213 Lichtenstein SN1*. But despite the best efforts of the team it only appeared in model form for testing purposes.

In the summer of 1943 development began of the wide search radar *FuG 220 Lichtenstein SN2*. This used the transmitter, receiver, and switching system of the *Lichtenstein S* but on a new frequency of 91 MHz, and the display unit had two screens for bearings and height, the latter using points of light to indicate every 2 kilometres. Two series of this model were introduced: The 'A' system employed vertical dipoles set side-by-side on the left wing for bearings, while for height-finding a pair of horizontal dipoles set one above the other were mounted on the right wing. The 'B' system made use of four sets of vertical dipoles mounted in a square configuration on the nose. Height-finding was obtained by the parallel switching of the horizontally-lying antennas, and similar switching of the vertical pair was used for bearings. And although this arrangement resulted in a smaller search-angle, the improved beaming characteristics produced a longer range, targets up to 8 km being easily captured with only 2 kW of power. By October 1943 over 2,000 sets of this equipment had been produced.

During this period, however, the *Lichtenstein BC* and *C* systems were crippled by the Allied use of *Window*, and on top of this, the enemy raids of the winter of 1943 coincided with very bad weather which, with the unfavourable resolution of only 1,200 metres, meant that targets were often obscured. In an attempt to resolve the problem the *SN2* was replaced by the *FuG 202* or *212* and provision was also made for a wide-angle antenna.

From an operational viewpoint *Lichtenstein* was probably the most effective of all German airborne radars of its type. It had its greatest success on the night of 30 August 1944 when 95 Allied bombers out of a total of 795 were shot down. This is perhaps understandable because by early 1944 the *Lichtenstein SN2A*, *SN2B* and *SN2C* all had improved close resolutions of between 300 and 500 metres, but the *SN2*, working between 73 and 81 MHz, soon fell foul of Allied jamming. An interesting point is that the dipoles of the *Lichtenstein SN2* were at this time the subject of much discussion in which it was decided to shorten their phsyical lengths by the use of base loading coils, but in spite of this their length was still so long that they had to be mounted diagonally. In a version called the *Lichtenstein SN 2D* rear-facing antennas were tested which were expected to give a forward reading as well, but it was found that they gave only the range and no direction.

By now a large number of Ju88 G's had been fitted with the new *Morgenstern* antenna. This was housed in a radome which decreased the air resistance by about 30%, and although direction-finding and bearings were still determined by parallel switching in the classic method, the gain was very small because the elements were not half-wave dipoles. A design known as the *Morgenstern 2* which used cross-over half-wave dipoles with only one reflector or director was also examined, but as this was for higher frequencies it only found success with the *Neptun* systems. During the final weeks of the war a few Ju88 G's were fitted with additional antennas above and beneath the fuselage so that the entire area around the aircraft could be scanned, but useful as this idea was it had only very limited service as by now all frequencies of the *Lichtenstein SN2* were firmly jammed.

In a further attempt to combat jamming, frequencies of 64 and 116 MHz were tried, and a system similar to the *Lichtenstein S* but without height-finding was also tried on 52 MHz. They even came down to 34 MHz but information about the antennas is no longer available. Research was also carried out

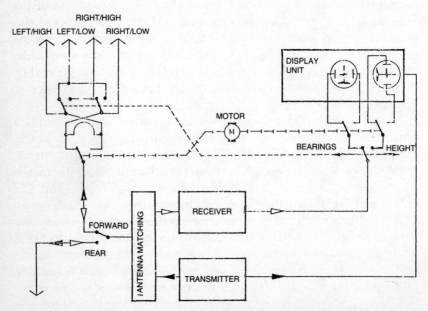

Figure 26 Simplified layout of the *FuG 228 Lichtenstein SN3* (*Fritz Trenkle*).

with a version of the *Lichtenstein SN2* with a screen only for the pilot, but the idea was short-lived. In early 1944 a bid was made to design an equipment with a variable tuning range between 100 and 158 MHz, but this brought in its wake a number of problems with antenna matching and any number of curious antenna patterns.

The last of the series was the wide-search *FuG 228 Lichtenstein SN3* with 20 kW of pulse power and a close resolution of between 220 and 250 metres, although the range was little better than 8 km. Both transmitter and receiver had in-flight selectable frequencies between 100 and 125 MHz, and the antennas, apart from being broadband versions, were similar to those of the *Lichtenstein SN2*. Later, a single screen display unit was provided which was adjustable for bearings and height, and a half-active system was included for homing in on enemy jamming transmitters. Unfortunately the system was plagued with problems and only one satisfactory model was produced in early 1945, and this brought the *Lichtenstein* series to an end.

*

The British first learned of the *Lichtenstein* equipment from a talkative prisoner of war in April 1941. Then in August a Me110B was believed to have shot down a British bomber with its aid. But by now it was quite easy for the British to monitor German radio telephony transmissions between their fighters and ground control, and they heard repeated mentions of the phrase *Kleine Schraube* (Little screw) and soon understood this was the coded order for the fighter to orbit a ground beacon. During 1942 increasing use of the term *Emil-Emil* was made, and this was taken to mean that the fighter had been guided by ground radar near enough to the bomber for the fighter to locate it with its airborne radar.,

It did not take Jones long to realise that the frequency of this equipment could soon be found by mounting a listening watch. Since German nightfighters were known to be operating in the Scheldt Estuary it was quite possible to hear them from the Suffolk coast, and soon transmissions were heard around 490 MHz which clearly came from moving sources.

He reasoned that it was likely that this frequency was used only by coastal nightfighters because the Germans would know that the transmissions could be detected at this range. In his view a different frequency would be used further back in Germany and the occupied countries, and it was vitally important to find it out in order to prevent bomber losses. As he also knew that the Germans had set up a heavy defensive system of nightfighters and ground radars known as the *Kammhuber Line* (see later) it became literally a matter of life or death for British bomber crews. One solution was obvious. A pair of Mosquitoes would have to be equipped with special monitoring systems and, relying on their speed, risk the German defences to find the frequencies.

What happened next is one of the most peculiar if not pathetic incidents in the annals of Bomber Command.

Jones approached Air Chief Marshal Sir Arthur 'Bomber' Harris, Commander-in-Chief of Bomber Command, and after fully explaining his reasons, asked for a couple of Mosquitoes, whereupon Harris referred him to his Deputy, Air Vice Marshal R.H.M. Saundby.

Saundby was renowned throughout the RAF for his eccentricity, and in order to get what he wanted Jones had to pretend to enjoy Saundby's interest in the *Daily Mirror* cartoon strips, display politeness throughout a lecture on fly fishing, and finally appear to wax enthusiastic over his set of model trains, all the while trying to cultivate this officer's astonishing whims in order to get him into the right frame of mind before actually asking for the aircraft. His patience won in the end for Saundby eventually agreed to let him have them.

But as Jones points out:

> It would be pleasant to record that the Mosquitoes were forthcoming within a week of my visit to Bomber Command; but this was not so. Since they would have to be allocated to the signals organisation that was operating the listening flights, I handed the Bomber Comand promise over to them, and awaited results. Unfortunately the Mosquitoes were still not available some two months later, and it was decided to risk one of the Wellington aircraft, which were much slower, in front of a nightfighter in the hope that the operator who was listening for the nightfighter transmissions would be able to give enough warning for the Wellington to escape.

The sequel to this was one of the bravest deeds of the war.

Early in the morning of 3 December 1942 a Wellington of No. 1473 (Wireless Investigation) Flight took off to accompany a bomber raid on Germany, and an hour or so later, as it was returning home, Pilot Officer Harold Jordan, the specialist radio monitoring operator, detected weak signals on the expected frequency. After warning the rest of the crew he drafted a coded signal giving the frequency and pulse-rate of the enemy radar and handed it to the wireless operator, Flight

Sergeant Bigoray, for transmission. As Bigoray dispatched the signal the radar transmissions increased in strength, almost saturating Jordan's receiver, and he warned the crew that an attack was imminent. Almost at that moment cannon shells hit the aircraft. The pilot, Pilot Officer Paulton, tried evasive action as the rear gunner, Sergeant E. Vachon, fired over a thousand rounds back, until his turret was put out of action and he himself was hit in the shoulder. Eventually the nightfighter broke off the attack, but the Wellington was badly damaged. Jordan had been hit in the arm, but managed to monitor the radar transmissions throughout the attack and to warn the crew of each approach of the enemy, and at the same time draft a second signal for transmission by Bigoray before being wounded in the jaw and the eye. The Wellington was in a sorry state. The port engine throttle had been shot away, and the starboard throttle was jammed. The starboard aileron and both airspeed indicators were out of action, and four of the six-man crew were injured.

Although badly wounded, Bigoray sent Jordan's signal time and time again in the hope that someone might hear it. It was in fact heard and an acknowledgement was sent, but Bigoray's receiver was too damaged to hear it. He continued to send his message until nearly seven o'clock in the morning. On approaching the English coast Paulton decided that the aircraft was too badly damaged to risk a crash landing and prepared to put it down in the sea near the coast. Since he could not know whether Jordan's message had got through, and since Bigoray's injuries were such that he might not be able to escape from the Wellington before it sank, Paulton decided to fly inland and have Bigoray pushed out with his parachute with his vital information in case the aircraft and its remaining crew were lost in the sea. At the escape hatch Bigoray remembered that he had not screwed down his morse key to provide the continuous note for the direction-finding stations to track the aircraft, and painfully crawled back to do it. Paulton then returned and ditched in the sea a few hundred yards off Deal where, fortunately, they were saved a few minutes later.

It had been an epic of cool observation, great gallantry and resourceful doggedness. For some days we did not know whether Jordan was going to lose his eye,[1] but the surgeons

---

[1] Jordan in fact lost the eye. Jones was told at the time that the surgeons had saved it, but this was incorrect. Only after publication of *Most Secret War* did Jones learn the truth. Jordan camouflaged his loss by wearing his RAF cap at a more jaunty angle. Jones. Letter to the author.

managed to save it. He received an immediate Distinguished Service Order, the next thing to a Victoria Cross. Paulton was awarded the Distinguished Service Cross, and Bigoray the Distinguished Service Medal. The last gap in our understanding of the German night defences had been closed.

The finding of the British H₂S radar not only enabled Telefunken to design other systems, but to build an improved magnetron for airborne radar delivering 20 kW of power on 3,300 MHz (9 cm). This was employed in their panoramic search radar *FuG 224 Berlin A* which, despite its bulky laboratory construction due to the use of ancillary broadcasting type valves, was considerably lighter and smaller than the British original. The antennas were four ceramic stub radiators mounted in a *Plexiglas*[1] housing beneath the fuselage and rotated at 400 rpm, emitting a narrow fan-shaped pattern. The prf was 1,500 Hz and the echoes were displayed on the screen as points of light which made up an electronic map of the area being scanned, range measurement being achieved by an adjustable concentric scale for ranges up to 60 km. For height finding a second screen was provided with a horizontal timebase line displaying traces in the customary way. Bearings were of course simply read from the scanning screen directly.

Another development that appeared at this time (1943) and with a fair degree of optimism, employed a special roll-up map and the mechanical computer *X-Uhr*. These were intended to be used with the *Berlin* system to form the basis of a new blind bombing method, but as the Germans were more concerned with defence at this time, the higher authorities informed the scientists that the device was not entirely appropriate.

Higher hopes were held out for a system with much improved resolution when, in 1944, the US 3 cm H2X radar fell into German hands. A model was designed and produced called the *FuG 241 Berlin D*, in fact this was on the production line in early 1945 but never delivered in any quantity due to the now rapidly deteriorating war situation. In fact, the use of centimetric wavelengths of this order was not thought to be urgent, although in the summer of 1943 a British Mark VIII radar was recovered from a Mosquito that had crashed in shallow water near the French coast, and was given the code-name *Grille*. After several months of discussion it was decided to go ahead and use it as the basis of a new development called the *FuG 240/1 Berlin N1A*. This made use

---

[1] *Plexiglas* was the German equivalent of Perspex.

Antenna arrangement for the *FuG 220b Lichtenstein SN2b* (*Fritz Trenkle*)

Display unit of the *FuG 220 Lichtenstein SN2* in a Me110 G-4 (*Fritz Trenkle*)

Morgenstern antenna (*Fritz Trenkle*)

The *Morgenstern* antenna on the nose of a Ju88 G-6 (*Fritz Trenkle*)

Display screen of the *FuG 224 Berlin A* airborne panoramic radar showing the *Scharmützelsee* and surrounding areas. Inset the additional height screen used in conjunction with this radar (*Fritz Trenkle*)

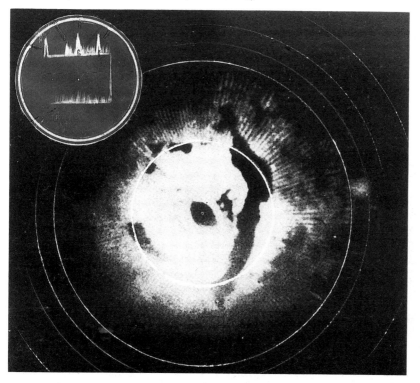

Above left Display unit and control box of the *FuG 224 Berlin A* in a FW200 (*Fritz Trenkle*)

Left Magnetron LMS 10 (right) copied from the British CV 76 9 cm H_2S magnetron. Left, the disc triode LD 9 delivering 150 watts continuous wave at 1500 MHz (*Fritz Trenkle*)

Above Antennas of the *FuG 218 V2 Neptun V2* on the nose of a Me262 B-1 (*Fritz Trenkle*)

Right Dr Hans Plendl (*Fritz Trenkle*)

Far right General Kammhuber (*Fritz Trenkle*)

FuG 350 Z   FuG 16 Z

Left Me109 G-6 fitted with the *FuG 350 Z Naxos Z* radar warning equipment (antennas in radome) and the antenna for the IFF equipment *FuG 16 Z* which was later combined with the *FuG 25* to form the *Neuling* system. The equipment shown here enabled an aircraft to talk to a U-boat (see text) (*Fritz Trenkle*)

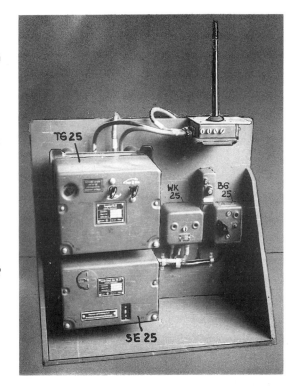

Left Antennas (under canvas) of the *FuMO 22 Seetakt* on the optical range-finder of the *Admiral Graf Spee*, 1939 (*Fritz Trenkle*)

Above right IFF set *FuG 25 Zwilling* (*Fritz Trenkle*)

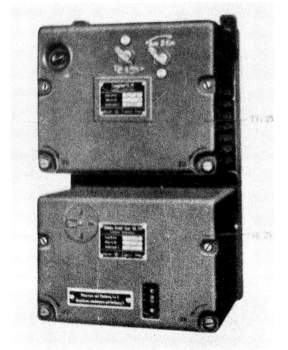

Right IFF set *FuG 25a Erstling* (*Fritz Trenkle*)

Left IFF set *FuG 25a Erstling* (open) and morse character selector key (*Fritz Trenkle*)

Below The *Graf Spee* scuttled (*Fritz Trenkle*)

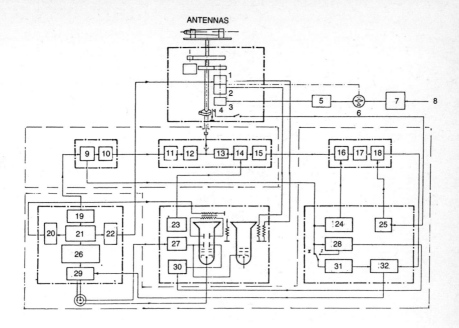

ANTENNAS

1. Goniometer	23. Auxiliary oscillator
2. Two-phase generator	24. Blocking-pulse generator
3. Rotator	25. Direction mark generator
4. Flight direction marking	26. Multivibrator
5. Steering relays	27. Screen trace amplifier
6. Slave compass	28. Height mark generator
7. Polar course control	29. Trace brightness pulse
8. From master-compass	30. Height mark amplifier
9. Multivibrator	31. Range mark generator
10. Pulse valves	32. Cross-fade system
11. Gas-drawn valves	
12. Magnetron	
13. Null point network	
14. Mixer	
15. UHF amplifier	
16. UHF amplifier	
17. Rectifier	
18. Low-frequency amplifier	
19. Synchronised pulses	
20. Saw-tooth voltage	
21. Saw-tooth voltage generator	
22. Saw-tooth current	

Figure 27 Layout of the *FuG 224 Berlin A* (*Fritz Trenkle*).

of a similar centimetric generation method to the *Berlin A*, the display unit of the *Lichtenstein SN2* and components from the *Pauke A*, but it had a completely new pulse-generation system. The antenna was a rotating dipole and 70 cm diameter paraboloid housed in a wooden casing, its drive mechanism also being used to power a rotary switch connecting the antenna to

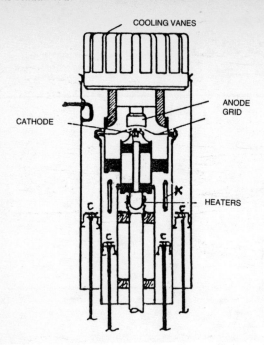

Figure 28 Diagram of the LMS 10 magnetron (20 kW at 3,300 MHz) used in the *Berlin* radar (*Fritz Trenkle.*)

show positions on the screen as 'above' 'right' 'below' and 'left' in this order, thus furnishing a similar presentation to that of the *SN2* but with much better beaming. The beamwidth was in fact ± 8° as compared to the *SN2*'s original 50°, but this improved pattern made target location more difficult especially when the enemy carried out defensive manoeuvres. For this reason a system was introduced in which the paraboloid could be rotated around 60° for bearings and from 30° to 70° for height-finding, the angle of the paraboloid being indicated to the pilot at any time on a screen with illuminated cross lines. The range was about 5 km and the close resolution about 350 metres. First employed by a nightfighter squadron in March 1945, it proved its value when ten enemy aircraft were shot down almost immediately.

The success of this equipment was at once followed up by a second version, the *FuG 240/2 Berlin N2*. This had a larger paraboloid which scanned 10 separate angles by electronic pattern rotation, and was largely used for testing new types of display screens including a 'sector-panoramic' screen something similar to those used for today's weather radar. The same type of display was used with its successor, the *FuG 240/3 Berlin*

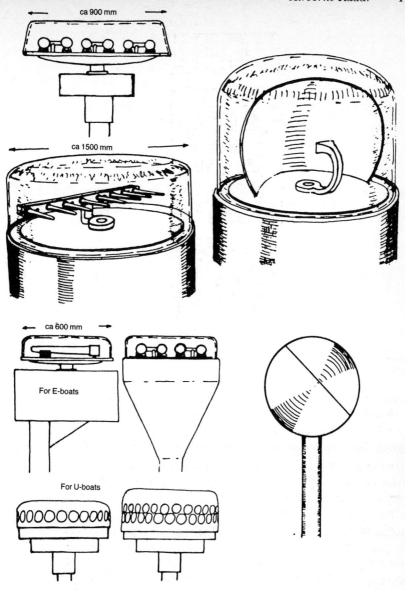

Top left: 6 and 8-element radiators for early *Berlin* equipment.
Top right: Horn antenna for the *FuMO 82 Berlin K.*
Bottom left: 4-element radiators *Bullauge* for E-boats and U-boats.
Bottom right: Antenna for the *FuMO 83 Berlin U.*

Figure 29 Antennae used in the *Berlin* system (*Fritz Trenkle*).

N3, but with a larger angle of about 60°, height-finding being achieved by its rotation around a pre-determined point. Neither of these systems, however, went into production because other developments showed more promise. Among

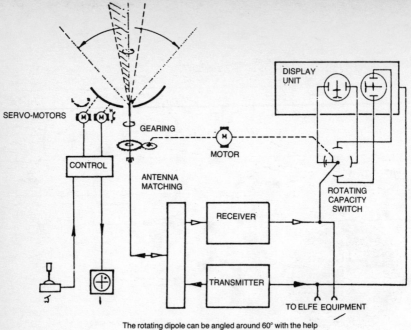

SERVO-MOTORS

GEARING

MOTOR

CONTROL

ANTENNA
MATCHING

DISPLAY
UNIT

ROTATING
CAPACITY
SWITCH

RECEIVER

TRANSMITTER

J

TO ELFE EQUIPMENT

The rotating dipole can be angled around 60° with the help
of the 'joystick' control 'J' and the indicator screen 'I'.

Figure 30 Layout of the *FuG 240* and *FuG 244 Berlin N4* equipment (*Fritz Trenkle*).

these was the successor to the *N3*, the *FuG 240/4 Berlin N4*, sometimes known as the *Rudolstadt H*, which was really nothing more than an unaltered *Berlin A* except that it had an antenna on top of the aircraft to give a panoramic view of the space above it. This antenna consisted of six ceramic stubs in a new 90 cm paraboloid of which great things were expected, but unfortunately the tailplane and cabin interfered with its pattern and difficulty was found in obtaining a satisfactory height indication. Code-named *Obertasse* (Cup), this antenna system was the subject of much debate in the latter days of the war, as was the whole question of pursuing the *Berlin* and *Neptun* systems.

It was also becoming obvious that good as the *Pauke A* system was, a better equipment was needed for the increasing number of heavy Allied bombing raids, the autumn of 1944 being a particularly bad time for the Germans. A version of the *Berlin N1* was therefore re-designed under the designation *FuG 222 Pauke S* and installed in nightfighters with a repeater screen on the instrument panel for the pilot. At the same time Dr Schmied of Telefunken developed the *Pauke Q* in co-operation with Werneuchen.

Complaints were now being made that although the *Berlin*

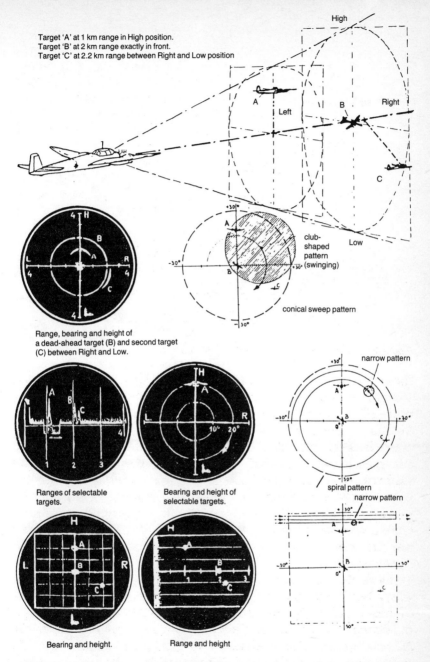

Target 'A' at 1 km range in High position.
Target 'B' at 2 km range exactly in front.
Target 'C' at 2.2 km range between Right and Low position

club-shaped pattern (swinging)

conical sweep pattern

Range, bearing and height of a dead-ahead target (B) and second target (C) between Right and Low.

Ranges of selectable targets.

Bearing and height of selectable targets.

narrow pattern

spiral pattern

narrow pattern

Bearing and height.

Range and height

Figure 31 Comparative representations of different targets and antenna sweep patterns with nightfighter radar equipment (*Fritz Trenkle*).

N1A gave very fair results, its all-up weight of 180 kg was really too heavy. The Telefunken team gave some thought to the problem and at the end of 1944 they came up with a much lighter system called the *FuG 244 Bremen 0*. This employed a high power magnetron which gave a range of 5 km and a close resolution of 200 metres, but in an attempt to reduce the weight by a further 70 kg by changing the prf from 1,000 to 500 Hz, the resolution became much worse. And as no easy remedy was possible without increasing the weight once more, and the war situation prevented more time being spent on the problem, all work on this model and the *Berlin N1A* was stopped even though over 100 sets had been produced. Among these the *Bremen* series were probably the most interesting. Designed for operation in the range 8.5 to 8.9 cm as opposed to the British 9 cm, it had been hoped to increase the range to 8 km by raising the power to 60, and later, 100 kW, but development of the necessary valves only came about in the last few days of the war. But it was clear that even in its early stages much better scanning and accompanying improvement of target indication could be obtained with the inclusion of the *Berlin N1A* sweep-system. Like the ground-installed panoramic radars a PPI screen was employed so that a forward target could be located and its range measured, this being achieved by the spiral scanning of the forward area through antenna rotation and a shift of a few degrees around its orbital axis so that through a series of 'steps' or 'openings' on a supplementary range screen, the angle positions could be measured by using the readings from both screens. As soon as a target had been selected it was locked on by an automatic tracking circuit which at the correct moment fired the guns.

A similar system based on captured Allied equipment and codenamed *Frankfurt* showed both lateral and height positions on one screen and gave the height once more, but now with the range, on another. And although not very much is now known about this system it is believed to have been the subject of experiments which showed promise. It was also discovered at this time that rectangular screens were better than round ones and these were developed for use with the *Frankfurt* and also with the *Berlin N2*.

The *Bremen* system was in fact succeeded by the *FuG 247 Bremerhaven*, originally known as the *Pauke SD*. This operated on 3 cm and had an improved resolution of between 2 and 3°. Spiral scanning with a conical pattern of 120° gave a range of 10 km irrespective of height and the system was intended as a substitute for visual location. For single-engined fighters this was used in conjunction with the automatic firing system *FuG 248 Eule* (Owl) operating on 1.6 cm with a range of 3 km depending on the height. Wave-guides built into the wings were rotated around the leading edge to provide automatic range-straddling, and although the expected delivery date was autumn 1945 a laboratory model with a 2 km range was in active service by February.

In December 1944 orders were placed with both Telefunken and Lorenz for a system called the *FuG 242 München (T/L)* and a similar equipment, the *FuG 246 München 0*. While little is now known about the full specification it is believed these were pulse radars working on a very high frequency with an angle resolution of 1° and a range of 100 km, so that the entire area below the aircraft up to very small ranges could be swept. Although ASV measures were well within its grasp it was considered more appropriate at this time for the location of tanks and armoured vehicles, and for this reason it was installed in the Ar234, the Me262 and the Do335.

Even colour tubes were used in at least one system. The night-fighter system *Schwabing* developed by Dr Schwartz of Atlas-Werke operated on 3,150 MHz with a pulse-power of 10 kW, and was intended as a sector-panorama search radar which would give a jet fighter pilot a quick general target indication before a more accurate location with another system. The relative flying height of the target was shown by a coloured band according to the sector flown, that is, if the target was at the same height as the fighter the screen was yellow, lower was green and higher was red. Again, it is unfortunate that fuller details of this are no longer available.

The systems so far mentioned were able to locate the enemy up to ranges of about 8 km, but pursuit in cloud or poor weather conditions was difficult because at about 100 metres the target was more often than not lost in the zero area. This poor close resolution problem was the subject of much research, and led in January 1944 to the development by Dr von Rautenfeld of the Ernst-Orlich-Institut at Danzig of what was called the Compensation System. This was a radar which operated on continuous waves and was given the name *Lichtenstein Danzig*, but because of confusion with the existing *Lichtenstein* the name was changed to the *Luchs* (Lynx). It employed an unmodulated transmitter and a receiver tuned to the same frequency, a small part of the transmitter energy being fed to the receiver over a compensating circuit in such a way that the amplitude and phase was used to 'quench' the receiving antenna. This condition was however altered at the return of an echo from a target so that the receiver detected not only the frequency of the echo, but also the higher frequency generated at approach speeds, in other words, the Doppler Effect. As the system worked best if the wing span of the target was close to a half-wavelength of the transmitter (and a wing-span of about 36 metres was usual) the *Luchs* generally operated on about 8.34 MHz with a power of 10 watts. (8.34 MHz = 35.97 metres.)

This model was first installed in a Ju87 and a Do17Z, the aircraft themselves acting as the transmitting antennas by being fed over a special coupling method. The receiving antennas were loops mounted at the ends of the wings. The Ju87 had a range of between 800 and 1,000 metres with Doppler swings of between 1 and 7 Hz, but with the Dornier the range was somewhat less, and in any case the system was badly distorted by heat from the engines.

The *Luchs* was also tested on the ground for detecting low-flying aircraft, prism antennas being used in the normal way for both transmitter and receiver, but aligned over an open stretch of land of about 300 metres with the compensation system in between. An aircraft flying at 600 feet alongside the antenna gave a very strong Doppler swing, and this was more pronounced at 1,800 feet in front of and behind the receiver, but even more gratifying was the appearance of a range measurement on a harmonic of the transmitter, which was all the more unexpected in view of the modest receiver selectivity.

Although this development took place in 1944 the principle was certainly not new. As early as 1939 a very similar method but without compensation had undergone research by Dr Plendl and Dr Netheler at Rechlin and was given the name *Raum-Such-Plendl* or *RSP* (Plendl Space Searching). In this system the transmitting and receiving antennas were connected diagonally to the flight path of the aircraft and employed reciprocal neutralising, by which method the reflected echo sounded an alarm.

The *Luchs*, however, also formed the basis of an experimental system called the *Kreuzblume* (Milkwort). This was the result of combining the *Luchs* with the *Dieckmann-Hall-System* (q.v.) where supplementary circuits were used for direction-finding to both sides and above and below the aircraft. Differential switching of horizontal loops served for bearing finding by using voltage comparison, and a similar method was employed for height finding by the use of vertical loops. Target indication was shown on the screen in the form of traces displayed from the centre outwards, to top, bottom, left and right, including intermediate positions. A number of flight tests confirmed that while the direction-finding was sharp enough for practical purposes, the degree of neutralisation was insufficient for useful ranges.

By 1943 the Germans had of course any number of ground radars which could easily distinguish between aircraft and stationary targets, but, as mentioned, these were often unsuitable for aircraft installation due to their size or for other reasons. And with the problem of poor resolution in mind, investigations were carried out by Telefunken into a system called *Erkner*, formerly known as the *Rudolstadt K*, which, through modifications and the introduction of new techniques including the Doppler system, was intended for the exclusive location of air targets. Unfortunately, very little progress was made with it, although the idea seemed sound, because the required angle of resolution of 0.1° was never reached. Dr Pöhlmann, who was in charge of research into this particular system, therefore made a proposal for what he called a 'genuine visual radio system' which would serve as a visual substitute at night or in bad weather by omitting the range measurement. The principle was to scan the area with continuous waves and to excite the receiver antenna with the higher frequencies resulting from electrical pattern swinging, little attention being required for the transmission time as the reflected energy from the targets gave their positions according to the timing of the returns. This idea gave good results during testing, but it is doubtful whether it actually saw service. An idea to include the blind firing of forward guns had to be shelved due to the poor war situation.

As the war drew to its close, Blaupunkt developed a search radar called the *Max A* for the guidance of anti-aircraft rockets. This used 5 watts of continuous waves on 7,700 MHz, an interesting feature being that the transmitter magnetron, an LMS 86, also generated a harmonic which was used in place of the receiver oscillator. The equipment used four diagonally directed ceramic stubs in a horn reflector which were coupled in succession to the receiver over a rotary switch, the four changing Doppler voltages being fed over relay circuits for the rocket guidance system. A very efficient form of double mixing ensured that any frequency variations of the magnetron, i.e., sum or product, were filtered out, so that the constant of the

300 MHz frequency changer was in no way affected. The stability of the receiver was accordingly very good.

A variation of this, known as the *Schuss-Max*, was also considered for a blind firing system, and a similar type with provision for automatic firing will be discussed later.

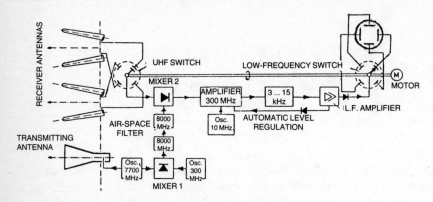

Figure 32 Layout of the search radar *Schuss-Max* (*Fritz Trenkle*).

CHAPTER EIGHT

Passive or Half-Active Radars

As the name implies, these do not use transmitters but only receivers and display units. They depend for their operation on transmissions from other sources such as the radar or jamming systems of the enemy, and for this reason are often known as half-active radars. As detection systems they have the advantage that their own positions are not betrayed by transmissions. On the other hand the lack of transmission means that while direction-finding is possible, range-finding is not, except in a general sense of comparative signal strength. For this reason such equipments were often used in nightfighters already equipped with active radar.

An early and simple form of these was the Blind Landing System pioneered by Lorenz called the *FuBL 1* which worked after a fashion by giving warning by a dial lamp, but the Luftwaffe, in contrast to the Navy, had no true VHF or UHF warning systems before the war, and it was not until British aircraft were equipped with jamming transmitters against the *Freya* that a demand was made for equipment to home on their transmissions. After experiments by the Research Regiment at Köthen and the FFO at Oberpfaffenhofen, a *Rostock* receiver and the antennas of the *Neptun* were employed by Siemens in their development of what was called the *FuG 221 Freya-Halbe*. With this equipment the antennas were fitted above and beneath the wings and canted diagonally forward, and the reflectors were adjusted so that a curved pattern was generated above and beneath the aircraft. The form of target indication was rather confusing. A point of light on the screen showed 'left' for returns on the left, but targets to the right appeared in the centre and 'high' and 'low' at the extreme right. On close approach to a target 'left' 'right' and 'high' now appeared at the top of the screen and 'low' at the bottom, and if all the points of light extended into traces of identical length it meant the target was dead ahead. If, however, the trace for 'high' was larger than the trace for 'low', then the target was ahead but slightly higher.

Surprisingly, this method found favour at Werneuchen where it was tested in early 1943 in a Ju88 and 25 sets were ordered.

There is a story that Kammhuber tried to delay the installation of these into aircraft for as long as possible because he believed a pilot might not use all his tactical air space if he depended on the method, but some people are of the opinion that Kammhuber was really thinking of the disorientating effect on the pilot. It is hard to reject the latter argument.

In 1943 a British bomber crashed in Holland and was found to contain a rear-warning radar called *Monica*. When the Siemens engineers had mastered their astonishment at the size of the equipment they promptly developed from it a smaller system called the *FuG 221a Rosendahl-Halbe*[1] which worked between 190 and 220 MHz, but for reasons of economy they used the same display unit as the *Freya-Halbe*. The antenna system used four stacked horizontal dipoles mounted left and right on the nose, the left and right elements being parallel switched for A/N bearings. For height-finding all the elements were connected over a form of phase-pulse switching to produce a vertical sweep pattern. The equipment gave a very good range of 100 km during tests but at ranges less than 4 km direction-finding was poor. This puzzled the engineers for some time until one of them discovered that the British jamming antennas were vertically polarised. And since an immediate rearrangement of the antenna system was impracticable, mainly because of the visual problems of the pilot and the formidable display system he had to work out, it was handed over to Rechlin for research into its possibilities as a searchlight radar.

In the meantime the British soon discovered that their system had been copied and employed their own sets less frequently.

The Germans naturally wished to learn as much as possible about other British equipments, particularly their ASV radars, and carried out further antenna experiments for this purpose,

[1] The aircraft had been shot down near Rosendahl in Holland.

together with a new receiver called the *FuMB/C* with a wider frequency range, but little is now known about this. The appearance of H$_2$S/ASV led to an immediate demand for a quick method of detection which Telefunken answered by producing the receiver *FuG 350 Naxos I* which was built from components of the *FuG 25 Zwilling* (qv). This operated between 2,500 and 3,750 MHz and could detect H$_2$S up to 8 km, and in some conditions even further. It employed a so-called 'finger' antenna, while the receiver included a very sensitive detector,[1] a band-pass filter and multistage amplifier. But the engineers were puzzled because during tests it was found to have a range of only 1 km, until, as in the case of the *Rosendahl-Halbe*, they discovered the British were using (at first) horizontal polarisation as opposed to their own vertical antennas. (Old Telefunken engineers, incidentally, are still of the opinion that the British should have used vertical polarisation in the first place.) But when the British decided to change to vertical polarisation, the design team were ready, for they had produced an improved system called the *FuG 350a Naxos 1a* with a triple 'finger' antenna whose elements were angled across each other at 45° for cross-polarisation in case they were caught napping again. Over 1,000 sets of this equipment were produced and installed on land and in U-boats.

Two months later a demand was made of the industry to tackle a problem of reception which had so far defeated them. The antenna of the *H$_2$S* system revolved in its circular sweep at 60 rpm which meant that it could only be detected at strength at a particular point of reception for only a very short time. Several firms addressed themselves to the problem but it was a Telefunken engineer who discovered that automatic direction-finding was possible if an antenna rotating twenty times faster than that of the *H$_2$S* was used. While they were developing this Telefunken also spent some time on the design of a new *H$_2$S* receiver called the *Steinzieger*, but this was later abandoned in favour of a new equipment known as the *FuG 350 Z Naxos Z*. This employed rotating ceramic antennas whose vertical fan-shaped pattern provided very good directional characteristics when mounted above an aircraft. The receiver used the same detector and bandpass system as the *Naxos 1* but was now fitted with a new low-frequency amplifier. A two-phase generator coupled to the antenna drive motor delivered two

---

[1] The detector was actually too sensitive. U-boats fitted with later models constantly dived to avoid British H$_2$S-equipped aircraft which were often many miles away.

90° in-phase shifted deflection voltages to the screen, this being the same type as that used in the *Neptun R2*. A blip appearing over its circular sweep gave the bearing of the enemy transmitter.

The system was tested at Werneuchen at the end of July 1943 and being found successful over 200 sets were ordered. These, together with a later model called the *FuG 350 Za/Zb Naxos Za/Zb*, were all in service by July 1944.

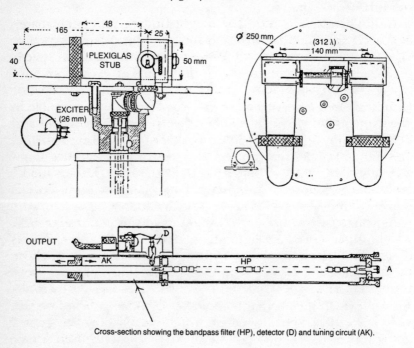

Cross-section showing the bandpass filter (HP), detector (D) and tuning circuit (AK).

Figure 33 Details of the direction-finding antenna *EA 350* used with the *FuG 350 Z Naxos Z* and all *Naxos* equipment to the *FuG Zc Naxos Zc* (*Fritz Trenkle*).

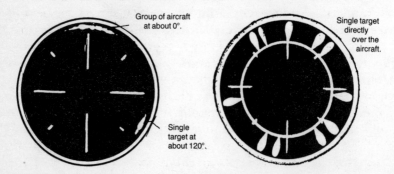

Figure 34 Screen displays of the *FuG 350 Z Naxos Z* and *FuG 350 Zc Naxos Zc* (*Fritz Trenkle*).

At about the same time the Research Department of the German Post Office relieved Telefunken of some of the burden by producing the *FuG 350 Zc Naxos Zc*. This was a somewhat simplified version using metal-envelope valves and gave (to their surprise) a range up to 50 km, whereupon they received an order for 600 sets which were installed in twin-engined nightfighters employed in the Illuminated Nightfighting Belt (described later) and also in two squadrons of Me109's.

Although no provision for height-finding had been made, and a certain amount of signal loss and curious stroboscopic effects appeared due to the dissimilarity in the rotation speeds of the H_2S and *Naxos* antennas, they were of great assistance when the aircraft's active radar was affected by *Window* or jamming, both these measures being particularly noticeable in the summer of 1944. By this time however between 100 and 200 sets per month were being delivered. Another system called the *FuG 350 ZR Naxos ZR* also made its appearance about this time, but apart from the fact that it used two additional horizontal dipoles on both sides of the tailplane little more is known about it.

As a countermeasure against the enemy's 3 cm radar *H2X* which appeared in April 1944, the *FuG 350 Zx Naxos Zx* was designed. This also employed ceramic antennas similar to those of the *Naxos Zc*. Later, a pair of rear-facing antennas were incorporated and it was then re-classified as the *FuG 350 Rx Naxos Rx*. A number of experimental equipments based on this system then followed, including a combination of the *Naxos Z* and *Zx* known as the *FuG 350 Zd Naxos Zd*. This used a new form of 3 cm antenna in a flattened parabolic reflector, and at the same time it was discovered that the range could be improved (and money saved) if the ceramic bandpass filters were omitted. These were well known for their dampening effect on the receiver and were also very vulnerable to fracture, especially when the aircraft landed. It was also found that the original 9 cm antennas would work quite well on the third harmonic and this discovery saved a great deal of production time and expense. About 100 *Zd* sets were made available for installation but exactly how many saw active service is hard to establish. It is believed the number must have been very small, since by the time they were ready the war was almost in its closing stages and the Luftwaffe had only enough fuel for about 50 aircraft.

Since the Naxos systems could not easily discriminate

between different frequencies in the 9 and 3 cm bands, an equipment was devised using the antennas and display unit of the *Naxos Z* and a new receiver designed by Dr Lämmchen of Blaupunkt in co-operation with Herr Sittner of Loewe-Opta. This was the *FuG 351e Korfu 812*, a superhet with a magnetron oscillator and very high sensitivity which, during tests in May 1944, gave a range of over 300 km. Its special tuning system permitted extremely fast detection of enemy transmissions and was especially useful in the 8.5 and 8.9 cm region in distinguishing between friendly and enemy transmissions.

In late 1944 Blaupunkt co-operated with Siemens to produce a new lightweight receiver with interchangeable components for operation in the 9 and 3 cm bands, but a number of problems cropped up which would have seriously delayed its production until Loewe-Opta joined in to help. In the event they managed to produce the *FuG 351 Zx Korfu Zx* which turned out to be one of the most precise equipments of the time.

Countermeasures against the American 3 cm radar *Meddo* were now also imperative and to this end the *FuG 351 Korfu V* was designed. This operated on 9,700 MHz with four ceramic antennas arranged in a square configuration but canted diagonally for 'high' 'right' 'low' and 'left' as in the *Flensburg* system. The display unit was jointly manufactured by Siemens and Blaupunkt who, during development, found a simpler method of display by removing the timebase line and arranging the circuitry to the deflection plates to correspond to the respective switching of the antennas. This resulted in points of light on the screen in a cross-shaped pattern corresponding to 'left' 'above' 'right' and 'below', the target being directly ahead when all parts of the cross were of equal length. The receiver, incidentally, was not a superhet but a TRF version fitted with an LG20 klystron and was also used in the *Max P* rocket guidance radar.

In 1944 plans were also made for what was called an Aperiodic Warning System which was given the name *Wim*. Three equipments were produced for this: the *FuG 360 Stieglitz* (Goldfinch) between 2,000 and 6,000 MHz designed by Pintsch, the *FuG 361* between 1,200 and 2,000 MHz by Telefunken and the *FuG 362* for 600 to 1,200 MHz by Loewe-Opta, but beyond these few details nothing is known about them.

Infra-red systems had been tried out before the war and several were developed later, but full details of these are not available. It is known that Siemens conducted research with an equipment called *Katze* based on a simple receiver with a fluorescent screen which was tested in 1942 by aircraft of KG 40. This had a range of about 800 metres and seemed to detect British infra-red searchlight systems fairly well, but the fluorescent screen (outside the aircraft) glowed so brightly that the British could see it quite easily.

A better device developed by AEG-Mayer and known as *Spanner* (Peeping Tom) was also tested in 1942. It is known that the receiver used photo-electric cells and fluorescent indicating valves (similar to the 'magic eye' tuning indicator) and that a 1000 watt infra-red projector was fitted on the nose of the aircraft which, in conjunction with electronic lenses, was believed to have a range of about 300 metres. Later versions including the *Spanner II* and *Spanner IIA/B* which appeared in 1943 were employed when the *Lichtenstein* was heavily jammed, and although 200 sets had been ordered only 15 were actually employed. Of an even later version, the *Spanner IV*, nothing is known.

CHAPTER NINE

IFF (Identification Friend or Foe) Systems

These systems are based on the principle of signals transmitted from a source such as a ship or an aircraft in such a way that identifies the source beyond doubt. They consist mostly of signals sent either independently of a radar system, or as part of that system, which will give identifiable traces or other effects on the screen or on another system of indication. In short, an IFF system is the electronic version of the sentry's time-honoured, 'Halt! Who goes there?' which, if followed by the correct password, is answered, 'Pass friend, all's well.'

IFF systems of the Luftwaffe were therefore based on such challenges sent by radio or radar and received by special recognition receivers in the aircraft, analysed, and then re-transmitted usually on a different frequency and often in the form of coded morse characters. With radar a slightly different form was employed. The response signal from the aircraft was received on the ground, processed, and then fed to the display unit on a common timebase line together with the normal radar returns, or it might be divided into several timebase lines where, in the case of several aircraft, the identity of a particular machine could be confirmed. For aircraft-to-aircraft recognition equipments were designed which worked either as separate recognition systems or in conjunction with the radar itself as 'challenge' transmitter and 'recognition' receiver, or in modern terms a transponder system.

Before the war names given to such systems as existed were not standardised. Terms such as 'Pulse-Repeater', and 'Pulse-Relay Transmitter' or 'Answer-Beacon' were common, and these were very simple systems where the received 'challenge' signal was re-transmitted on the same frequency (responder) or on a different one (transponder). Sometimes frequency-conversion (transposer) was employed, where the received signal was mixed with a local oscillator and then transposed to the transmitter frequency. The term 'Recognition Equipment' was used at this time only for equipments employing special recognition pulses, but very few of these existed and in any case were not very practicable.

The question of IFF systems for the Luftwaffe was first raised in 1938 at a meeting of the High Command which had been convened to discuss the development of radar for this branch of the Services. The proceedings were distinguished by a total lack of agreement between the Luftwaffe and the Navy over the allocation of frequencies (a matter never resolved then and seldom at any time during the war) but for some reason the discussion became drawn away from the point of the meeting and turned to the demands of the Flak (then controlled by the Army) for radar. Only after this matter had been dealt with were Martini's requests for IFF systems given any consideration, and then only after the members demanded proof that they were needed. Agreement was finally reached after Martini furnished evidence from tests showing that the simultaneous location of several aircraft by the existing ground radar called

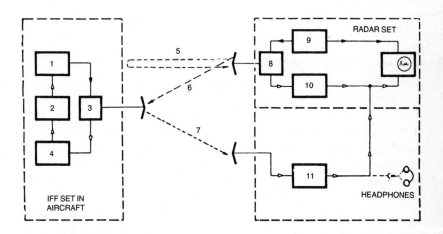

1. IFF transmitter	7. IFF response (recognition) signal
2. IFF recognition pulse generator and decoder	8. Antenna coupling
3. Antenna coupling	9. IFF transmitter at radar station
4. IFF receiver	10. Radar receiver
5. Radar beam	11. IFF ground receiver
6. IFF challenge signal	

Figure 35 Principle of the IFF equipment *FuG 25 Zwilling* as used with the *Würzburg* radars. IFF indications are given over headphones as shown (*Fritz Trenkle*).

for a more positive method of identification than was available at the time.

Even then, it was not until much later that the industry was called upon to provide these systems. Gema produced an early equipment called the *Stichling* (Stickleback) on 125 MHz which was intended for use with their *Freya*, and it is believed that another equipment (classification unknown) was designed for the early *Würzburgs* on 53 cm, but little more is known about this, except that Martini put in a demand for 3,000 sets which were never forthcoming. The only equipment known to be produced at this time was the *FuG 25 Zwilling* (Twin) (qv) which appeared at the same time as the *FuSE 62 Würzburg*, with a receiver working between 554 and 556 MHz and a transmitter on 160 MHz and was manufactured in large numbers. The receiver had very low sensitivity as it was only a TRF circuit with a diode detector and LF amplifier, and the transmitter delivered only 1 watt, nevertheless at the beginning of 1940 all aircraft were fitted with this system. A challenge signal was sent by the *Würzburg* on a special pulse-follower frequency of 5 kHz[1], and in case of breakdowns another signal with different characteristics could be sent on the same frequency. On being received by the aircraft the signals were analysed and then re-transmitted on a carrier modulated by morse characters, these being effected by a cam-switch mechanism set by insertable keys to operate a series of 10 contact-breakers so that any number and combination of morse signals could be selected. The recognition receiver used here was the *E 62 Steinzieger*.

In the middle of 1942 this system was modified to become the *FuG J1 Zwilling*, sometimes known as the *Hauptling* (Chieftain), which gave very good service during the British raids on Berlin. It operated on similar lines to its predecessor but the *Würzburg* was now adapted to include a time-lag circuit corresponding to the running time of the aircraft's equipment.

---

[1] The use of this prf meant of course that the time-base would not be indicating correctly for normal radiolocation purposes, and in fact the received recognition signal was indicated audibly over a loudspeaker or a pair of headphones. This loss of range indication was however only temporary since the radar could be quickly switched back to its customary 3750 Hz prf when required. The main problem with the system was that it only indicated that a friendly aircraft was in the vicinity, but it is possible that the 1 watt of power for the aircraft's IFF transmitter was chosen for this reason, i.e. that the aircraft would have to be relatively close for its signals to be heard. But undoubtedly the system had its weaknesses and for these reasons was quickly superseded by the *Zwilling*.

At the same time the display unit was modified so that returning recognition singals were displayed on the screen to the right of the normal radar returns. A range of between 20 and 30 km was customary with this system but this was often exceeded in good conditions.

A further development of this system was the *FuG 25 J2 Zwilling J2*. This operated with a receiver range of 554 to 566 MHz as before but without precise recognition keying. Unfortunately very little is now known about it except that its range is believed to have been up to 95 km, but in any case it never went into production.

In 1940 it was clear that the *Stichling* system was not really good enough, and two Gema scientists, Dr Brinker and Herr Preikschat, turned their attention to a laboratory model they had begun to design in late 1939. This was the *FuG 25a Erstling* (First child) which used the same frequencies as the *Stichling* but had a transmitter power of 600 watts. And as problems had been encountered with the receiver it was decided to change this to a superhet. They spent a great deal of time on the project but other problems cropped up, and although it was sent for official testing in 1941 it was only good enough for production by July 1942. Designed for long-range employment by the early warning system of the *Flugmelddienst* (Observer Corps) in conjunction with the *Freya*, it incorporated a special ground recognition receiver called the *Gemse* working on 165 MHz.

When Rechlin tested the *Erstling* they found it had a range of 100 km, and although it still had problems it was used in 1941 for research into what was called the *Erstling* System for fighter guidance devised by Dr von Hauteville. *Freyas* and *Würzburgs* fitted with the system enabled the range and position of the fighters to be determined while radio-telephony guided them to the enemy bombers. This method was used on the Channel coast in the summer of 1942 with some success, but in other locations the radio-navigation device known as the Y-System was given preference due to its faster operation. At the end of 1943 von Hauteville and Herr W. Kersten used the *Erstling* in their development of the *EGON* System (*Erstling Gemse Offensive Navigation*) for pathfinder aircraft. This worked originally on a split mode of operation. In the *EGON 1* system the pin-pointing of aircraft from a ground radar was not very accurate, but by obtaining measurements from two positions about 150 km apart with the *EGON 2* system the data could be transmitted to the plotting table of the *EGON 1*, which now functioned as a guidance system enabling any number of courses to be tracked. Many variations of this went into production in the summer of 1944, but as by that time the Allies were constantly jamming the radio-telephony links between the ground control and aircraft a series of command signal additions were developed which were fed to the receiver in an attempt to overcome it.

Despite its earlier problems the *Erstling* gradually matured into a reliable system especially in areas of concentrated radar positions, but when the Allied jamming grew worse it had to be modified for the so called 'scattered' frequencies of the *Wismar* System. This meant that additional challenge transmitters, recognition receivers, and their corresponding disruption to the industry which, in any case, was now struggling to meet its normal demands.

With the Navy circumstances were different. At sea, as a rule, they used only a single radar network and only simple ship-to-ship systems such as the *FuME 1 or 2 Wespe g* (Wasp) were employed whose challenge, recognition and re-transmission frequencies were similar. These systems were designed by Elac and operated on a simulaneous transmission and reception principle. A fairly simple regenerative receiver with no RF stage was employed, the idea being that its lower selectivity would enable signals over a wider range to be received than would be the case with a more selective set. The received signals together with the oscillator frequency of the detector were mixed and then fed to the transmitter, which in turn re-transmitted them with a power of 300 watts, giving a range of some 15 km.

With *Seetakt* radar the matter was even simpler because challenge transmitters and recognition receivers were not required. The radar itself could be tuned over a fairly wide range from 361 to 389 MHz and 353 to 429 MHz, and a simple motorised continuously-tuned system was used for this purpose. A similar principle was used for ship-board Flak whose radar employed the same frequencies as *Seetakt*. As a range of about 30 km was considered adequate they could economise by not using the *Erstling*.

In February 1942 Wega came up with an interesting contribution in the shape of the *Biene* (Bee). This system had no classification number but worked between 550 and 570 MHz with a range of 65 km, and was designed for use with Flak radars such as the *Würzburg*. It employed a very simple super-regenerative receiver with a separate oscillator and was often used in combination with the *Erstling* when the system was then known as the *Neuling PRK*. If required, it could after some modification be also used with the *Seetakt* on 368 MHz.

Unfortunately, although the principle was sound, the system was plagued with difficulties when Allied jamming began in earnest, so on 24 September 1942 the decision was made to design a new version called the *Neuling-Super*. This made use of two superhets on 560 and 368 MHz respectively and a transmitter on 590 MHz, but no sooner had the system reached a promising stage when a demand was made that it should conform to the *Wismar* requirements, and for this purpose a new recognition receiver for 590 MHz was required, together with a new transmitter. These duly appeared under the designation of the *Bodenanton 53* and *Bodenanton 80*, but despite very careful design and a great deal of time and trouble in the laboratory these brought no very great benefit.

At the beginning of the nightfighter campaign of 1942-1943 a demand was made for a reciprocal IFF system for fighters. As a temporary measure while the details were being thrashed out, a ban was placed on attacking any twin-engined enemy aircraft in case of mistakes, and this prohibition (which is still discussed today by those who remember it) was the stimulus for the designers and engineers to push ahead as quickly as possible. They therefore examined all nightfighter radars and finding that the *Lichtenstein* rear-warning system and similar equip-

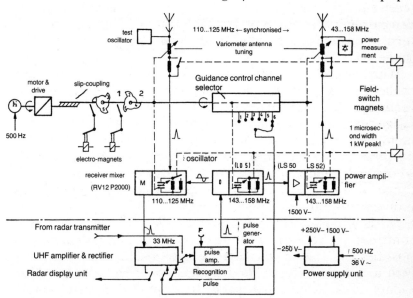

Figure 36 Simplified diagram of the *FuG 226 Neuling* IFF set (*Fritz Trenkle*).

ments were in general use in the appropriate type of aircraft, they thought that the *Erstling* system might be used in them if the *Lichtenstein*'s transmitter could be modified to work on 125 MHz, though additional antenna problems could be expected. They went ahead with this idea but found that the receiver could not cover the required frequencies without a great deal of modification. Lorenz, however, came to the rescue with a recognition receiver on 156 MHz called the *Lichtzieger*[1]. This was a five-valve set originally designed in two models for experimental purposes and the engineers cheerfully continued with their work in ignorance of the fact that plans had already been made to change the frequency of the *Lichtenstein* to 330 MHz, thus making it even more difficult to convert to 125 MHz. And to add insult to injury they were never told that in any case the *Lichtenstein* was about to be replaced by the *Neptun R*. They turned their attention to the *Bordanton S* on 125 MHz and even carried out experiments with the *Bordanton 53 S* and *Bordanton E* on 560 and 590 MHz respectively, but these were really nothing more than experimental projects and the original problem was never solved.

In December 1942 Martini convened a meeting to discuss the possibility of substituting the Flak's *FuG 25 J1 Zwilling* for the *Neuling-Super*, and using the *Zwilling* for air-to-air IFF. It was agreed that the *Zwilling* could be employed if it were fitted with an addition called the *Kuh-Gemse*, but air-to-air IFF might in any case need the *Erstling* system as a 'technical tactical requisition'. This was a euphemism for the German fear that their IFF might be used by the enemy in the same way that the Germans were making use of the RAF's IFF as in the *Flamme* system, or perhaps more accurately, if the enemy were to use it they might wake up to the fact that the Germans had also been doing so for some time.

A minor incident which probably deserves a place in German military history occurred in January 1943 in the Bay of Biscay. An aircraft was testing a system in which the *Neptun* receiver had been combined with the *Zwilling* to form the *FuG 16/25 Neptun-Zwilling*, the receiver working between 36.5 and 42.3 MHz. During these trials it picked up a U-boat's transmissions on its VHF radio-telephony set *Lo 10 UK 39* on about 37.8 MHz and was thus able to use it as a recognition system. From a technical viewpoint this was nothing remarkable – except that it happened to be one of the very few instances when a German

[1] Light indicator.

ship was able to communicate with a German aircraft by radio. Even in the middle of the war the Navy, it seems, was not always on speaking terms with the Luftwaffe …

During the course of further discussions in 1943, a proposal by von Hauteville was adopted to order no new equipment but to design a new system to replace the *Zwilling*. This was to have ten interchangeable transmitters and receiver frequencies, and in autumn Dr Klöpfer of Lorenz was commissioned to design it. This was the *FuG 226 Neuling* whose challenge transmitter was synchronously pulsed with the transmitter of the airborne radar and delivered a pulse-power of 1 kW on 110, 113, 116, 119, 122, and 125 MHz, while the receiver operated on 143, 146, 149, 152, 155 and 158 MHz. Range measurement was co-ordinated with the recognition system by paralleling the receiver's output with that of the radar receiver and feeding the result to the display unit. During recognition reception the transmitter frequency was shifted 20 times per second simultaneously with the receiver frequency, recognition keying delivering two morse characters with three-second gaps. By autumn 1944 over 300 sets had been delivered but by the end of the year this dwindled to only three equipments as a result of other demands on the industry. These sets, incidentally, together with their blueprints and other documents were seized by the Americans during the invasion and sent to the USA.

The employment of enemy IFF signals was however accomplished by combining the *Neuling* with a standard nightfighter radar so that both the nightfighter and the enemy could be distinguished if both were within range by observing the enemy's IFF signal on the nightfighter's screen, but this method had several disadvantages, not least of which was the appearance of extraneous traces which were very troublesome. To overcome this a centimetric version of the *Neuling* was produced with rotating direction-finding antennas which not only solved the problem but also enabled the system to be used for fighter-guidance, navigation and blind-landing purposes. But after much research had been carried out it was decided to go ahead with another system called *Frischling* (Raw Beginner) which was also designed by Klöpfer at Lorenz and intended for use with a later mark of the *Neuling* called the *Neuling K*. For direction-finding co-ordination of the recognition signal it used a 1 kW transmitter with an LD 70 disc valve, rotary direction-finding antennas, and a direct-conversion (homodyne) receiver with two RF stages for operation on 2,500 MHz. The system sent out challenge pulses on VHF and centimetric ranges simultaneously, and the challenged aircraft responded with recognition signals only when it received both sets of pulses. This was, however, a somewhat complicated method and they searched for a simpler solution, preferably one whereby the aircraft's radar would send the challenge signals, leaving only a requirement for an additional receiver which, of course, would have to cover the new frequencies of later marks of airborne radar.

Such a system was designed by Dr Gossel of Lorenz and given the classification *FuG 229 ABC Frischling ABC*. This covered the following frequencies: (A) = 300 to 600 MHz, (B) = 2,600 to 3,050 MHz, and (C) = 8,050 to 13,000 MHz. The 'A' model used a TRF receiver with a diode in the first stage followed by a 4-valve LF amplifier (one EF 14 and four RV 12P 2000's). This and the 'C' model employed omni-directional antennas and were energised by the power supply of the *Neuling*. As with the earlier *Frischling* a response was transmitted only on the reception of the different frequencies of the *Neuling* and *Frischling ABC* systems. The 'B' design for some reason was never used.

At this point it is convenient to return to early 1943 when aircraft were fitted with the *Zwilling* and ground radars equipped with the *Kuh-Gemse* system. Preferential treatment was supposed to be given to the nightfighter guidance system, but long delays occurred in the summer because of the need to adapt equipments for the different frequencies of the *Wismar* System, as mentioned, and to find ways of overcoming *Window*. To meet these requirements and at the same time to avoid interference with the *EGON* nightfighter guidance system, a series of the *FuG 25a Zwilling* was produced for operation on 119 and 154 MHz which proved of great value up to the end of 1944 when it was replaced by the *FuG 25c Roter Erstling*. This had a 400 watt transmitter and a receiver which could be tested in flight by its own in-built test transmitter. For its easier recognition by ground radars a pulse circuit was included which also generated the recognition morse signals with a three-second gap between them.

Good as this system was, problems of component supply at this time were such that the production line would have been seriously disrupted, so it was decided to go ahead with a system designed by Herr Köhler of Telefunken called the *FuG 225 Biene W* which used parts readily obtainable from the *Neptun* equipment. This used transmitter and receiver frequencies between 416 and 580 MHz which could be alternately used over another system known as *Wobbelbiene* for the swift changing of frequencies. This equipment, which was used in conjunction with the *FuG 25a Erstling*, was installed in twin-engined fighters and also in reconnaissance aircraft and used a special omni-directional antenna which could be either horizontally or vertically polarised. This radiator was in some respects similar to the *FuMB Ball* antenna, being a ring dipole with two vertical stubs. The equipment worked as an IFF system with the *Würzburg* Flak radar and also with the Navy's *FuMO 61/65 Hohentwiel-Seetakt* (qv) but without an additional challenge transmitter or recognition receiver. Proposals made at this time for its employment with the *Lichtenstein BC* and *C1* were not taken up since the *Lichtenstein SN2* and the *Neptun V* were shortly to take their places.

By autumn 1944 the *Biene* was replaced by a simpler system called the *FuG 243 Hohentwiel-Biene-Bord* designed by Wega. This had a variable-frequency range between 545 and 565 MHz and was supplied exclusively for use with the *FuG 200 Hohentwiel* in reconnaissance aircraft. The *Hohentwiel* was equipped with horizontally polarised antennas for ship-board use or on land as required, with the exception of the *FuMO 61* and *62* versions of the *Pantowiel* which used vertical antennas at all times.

Shortly after the appearance of this equipment, the Research Establishment at Travemünde conducted tests and came up with the idea of building it in a wooden cabinet with batteries and installing it on the foremast of the *Prinz Eugen*. This enabled the ship to undertake long-range IFF communications in bad weather and also to assist in the homing of aircraft fitted with the *Hohentwiel* at ranges up to 150 km. Although the equipment was later badly damaged in action it was used successfully for maintaining contact with convoys to which long-range aircraft could be directed. It was also used during February and March 1945 as a navigational aid in Norwegian waters where aircraft could be guided to special landing strips, or for the dropping of supplies to troops.

Earlier than this, at about the end of 1943, the Getewent Co (GTW) modified the Navy's *Wespe g* to produce a small series called the *Wespe f* on 125 MHz with 300 watts of power. Sometimes known as the *Biene f*, this was designed for ships in conjunction with the coastal *Freyas*, and though designed by GTW five sets were built by Siemens in 1944 to operate on 91 MHz. This was also known as the *Impulswiederholer* (Pulse-repeater) *Biene-Lang* system, and though designed for the

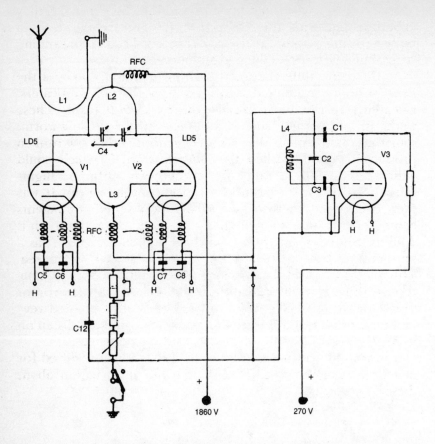

Figure 37 Circuit diagram of the oscillator and power amplifier stages of the *FuME 1 and 2 Wespe (G) (Fritz Trenkle).*

purpose mentioned it was mainly employed as an airfield approach beacon for aircraft fitted with the *Lichtenstein SN2*. While little is now known about it, it is believed to have been very similar to the *Biene SN3* which had a frequency range of 100 to 158 MHz and was installed in nightfighters fitted with the *Lichtenstein SN3*.

For tactical reasons blind-landing systems became even more important towards the end of 1944 and a number of these were designed. It was of course necessary that they should accommodate the *Lichtenstein*-equipped aircraft and the first to appear was the *Blindsleiche* (Slow-worm) for the guidance of aircraft fitted with the *Lichtenstein C1*. This was yet another unfortunate blunder on the part of a group of ill-informed scientists because the *Lichtenstein C1* had long been replaced by the *Lichtenstein SN2*, and to this day it is not clear how it came about. But in a last-ditch attempt to hide their mistake they experimented with the *Lichtenstein C1* and rebuilt it as a pulse-repeater system for use as a response beacon for landing strips, but it is doubtful if it had any success.

At the same time centimetric airborne radars such as the *Berlin* series were adapted as different types of pulse-repeaters, research into this being carried out by several firms. These were given names such as *Glühwürmchen* (Glow-worm) sometimes known as the *Wespe-Panorama*, and Telefunken produced a model called the *Glühwürmchen T* which could either be used as a range-finder between different flight-formations or on the ground as an approach-beacon. It was even considered for use as a recognition system for agents behind enemy lines, but whether it was actually used as such is doubtful. Lorenz were more practical and re-designed it as a pin-pointing beacon for aircrew who had ditched in the sea. This was a very useful equipment which employed a *Frischling* receiver and a small transmitter in a very strong waterproof case. Operating between 143 and 158 MHz it responded very well to the radar of a search aircraft which could also listen on its *Neuling* system.

It is also known that a number of radars were modified for meteorological purposes at this time but information about these is scanty.

CHAPTER TEN

The Radar of the German Navy

As mentioned in Chapter Two, 82 cm radar for shipboard or coastal employment was delivered as early as 1938, usually under the classification of *Dete 1*, then *Dete 101* and finally the *FMG 39 G (gB)*, the last letters denoting the antennas used and the methods of installation. The pulse power was between 1 and 8 kW and the prf was originally 2,000, then 1,000 and finally 500 Hz, all equipments using maximum direction-finding with separate antenna halves for transmitting and receiving. All these, and later marks, were grouped together under the general classification of *Seetakt*.

One of these equipments, the *FMG 39 G (gB) Calais*, known after 1942 as the *FuMO 1 Calais*, used the platform of a *Freya* with its antennas attached to a 2 by 6 metre framework, the upper half being used for reception and the lower for transmission. The range for naval gunnery was up to 20 km with a range accuracy of about 70 metres and a direction-finding accuracy of 3°.

In this year the pocket battleship *Admiral Graf Spee*[1] was fitted with a version of this system, the *FMG 39 G (g0) Calais*, and a cabin for the equipment and its 3 by 6 metre antenna was mounted above the optical range-finder on her foremast, thus enabling the data from both systems to be readily compared.

By November, identical equipment had been installed in the *Gneisenau*, the *Scharnhorst*, the *Admiral Hipper*, the *Blücher*, the

---

[1] The *Admiral Graf Spee* was officially an 'armoured ship' (*Panzerschiff*), equal to a heavy cruiser. The term 'pocket battleship' was a journalese expression coined to 'explain' the battleship-size 6 × 28 cm guns carried by this vessel which was made possible due to weight saving by using novel welding methods for the hull etc instead of riveting.

Admiral Scheer and the *Deutschland*, this latter being later renamed the *Lützow* by a superstitious Führer, lest a ship be sunk bearing the name of the Fatherland. But these installations proved a burden in the already over-crammed spaces of these vessels, so in the construction of the *Bismarck* large operating rooms were built on her foremast and at the stern to accommodate the *FMG 39 G (gP) Calais* and the antenna arrays of 2 by 4 metres. A similar model was also designed and fitted in the *Prinz Eugen* in 1940, but a year later it was removed and replaced with a passive radar.

For destroyers, and also originally for light cruisers, a simplified version known as the *FMG 39 G (gL) Calais* was employed. This had a rotating column mounted on the bridge to carry both transmitter and receiver with a 2 by 4 metre array arranged above, the display unit and auxiliary equipment being installed in the body of the ship. Such a model was built in the light cruiser *Nürnberg* and gave good service, though the range was correspondingly shorter than that of the larger ships, being usually of the order of 18 km. Destroyer ranges were of course even shorter because the antenna height was much lower.

Shortly after the beginning of the war, as a result of experience gained, Gema and the Communications Research Establishment soon had a production line of over 100 sets of the *FMG 40 G (g) Seetakt*. These were hardly distinguishable in appearance from the original sets which had been delivered in batches of six just before the war and which, with a pair of *Freyas*, were mainly employed on the islands of Heligoland, Borkum and Sylt for coastal defence. The new version, however, was used almost immediately for air defence and many installations were enclosed in walls where it was soon discovered that damage occurred very frequently to the horizontal antennas when the array was lowered or raised. For this reason some equipments were fitted with vertical antennas, and in a number of instances the antenna area was actually doubled, which resulted in a 30% increase in range. The *FMG 40 G (gD) (FuMO 3) Calais Zerstörersäule* (Destroyer Column) was a land version for installation in a bunker and used the rotating column of the *FuMO 21 Boulogne* to support the transmitter, receiver and the 2 by 4 metre antenna. This equipment was only used in small numbers and according to official German reports only eleven were employed on the French coast, and no photographs of these are known to exist.

In 1940 Gema also produce an equipment rejoicing under the name of the *Radattel* (Wheel-rattle) Direction-Finding

System. In this, the left and right halves of the receiving antenna were connected over a half-wave length of feeder to a motor-driven rotary switch in conjunction with a special deflection voltage supply delivered from a synchronised rotary contact-breaker, the resulting noise being responsible for the nickname *Radattel*. If during scanning operations the results corresponded to either of the extreme points of the feeder, in other words if the sum of the voltages of both halves of the antenna was present, an elongated lobe-pattern was generated. If, however, this occurred at the centre of the feeder a pair of lobes appeared, meaning that the antenna voltage was nulled out at a precise point between them.

This differential-voltage principle was continued during the further resolution of the plot, that is to say the pair of lobes grew smaller until only one very fine pair remained. To accompany this system a new display unit had been designed which included a double-beam tube, the top half of which displayed the normal indication trace while a pair of traces appeared on the lower half from a special sweep system using one of the deflection voltages of the rotary contact-breaker. If the central point of the double trace (corresponding to the pair of lobes) was exactly on an engraved line in the centre of the screen the antenna was then pointing directly at the target, and target movements to the left or right of this point produced an antenna minimum to conform with them. This system was widely employed with the existing *Seetakt* radars and was also incorporated into the design of later models, in the course of which the number of valves used rose from 25 to 38 not including rectifiers.

The Navy was dependent upon Gema for its radar equipment right up to 1942, but during this period Gema became seriously overloaded by their commitment to produce *Freyas* for the Luftwaffe. This burden did little to endear the Navy to their brothers-in-arms, but in any event Gema had no option but to ask Telefunken to come to the rescue, and in 1942 they began manufacturing the Navy's requirements under licence. But even this did little to increase the flow of systems for naval use. In fact, since the war experiences of 1941 the Navy had considered a completely new generation of radars, but now the war situation was such that this was out of the question and they had to be content with original models and such improvements to them as could be made from time to time.

And in case too much should be made of these shipboard

FuMO 23 Seetakt on the foremast of the *Bismarck* (*Fritz Trenkle*)

FuMO 26 Boulogne antennas with *Radattel* direction-finding on the *Prinz Eugen* (*Fritz Trenkle*)

Left Prinz Eugen showing radar antenna (*Fritz Trenkle*)

Right Equipment of the *FuMO 25 Boulogne* in the radio room of the *Prinz Eugen* (*Fritz Trenkle*)

Right FuMO 2 Calais coastal radar with doubled antenna area (*Fritz Trenkle*)

Left Antennas of the *FuMO 29 Seetakt* arranged round the conning tower of a type IX C 40 U-boat (*Fritz Trenkle*)

Below FuMO 52 Mammut-Cäsar long range radar (*Fritz Trenkle*)

radars (at least in their very early stages) it must be pointed out that so far as naval gunnery is concerned they seldom came up to the requirement of bettering the ship's optical range-finder, even though sometimes their range-measurement accuracy was much better, and of course they had the advantage of being able to locate the enemy in fog or by night. But this had to be set against other problems. For example, gunnery by radar in a rough sea was rendered difficult through the lively motion of the antennas, and this could only be remedied by the construction of expensive stabilising gear. This treatment was in fact given to an experimental *Würzburg Riese* installed in the *Togo* and proved quite successful, but the installation of the *Riese* itself in battleships was impracticable, although some small *Würzburgs* were occasionally used.

Radar in capital ships suffered from three major problems. First, the equipment was often susceptible to humidity and the resulting condensation badly affected its sensitivity, and second, (and more important) naval gunnery itself often put the set out of action after the first salvo. Third, in the early years at least, adequate training for the operators was unavailable and no skilled maintenance personnel were provided, all maintenance and routine servicing being carried out to the best of his ability by the Communications Officer or, as in most cases, by the Leading Wireless Telegraphist.

All these problems were eventually solved but in the early days of the war they were very troublesome. The situation was not helped by the known aversion of Hitler to capital ships, and it was well-known that the U-boat Arm was the favoured branch of the service. Gema had in fact produced two experimental models for U-boats at the beginning of the war but their size was prohibitive, and in any case priority had to be given to hydrophone equipment.

By 1941, however, the operational use of U-boats had so changed that demands were made for radar for all-weather conditions, especially in the East-African theatre, and because no new development could be undertaken at that time a *Seetakt* radar was substantially reduced in size and classified as the *FMG 41 G (gU) (FuMO 29)*. Even then it was so large that Gema were undecided at first whereabouts to install it in the U-boat allocated to them for testing purposes, and their final choice of next to the conning tower ladder was a source of innocent merriment to all in the U-boat service who heard about it, because torrents of water fell on it when the hatch was opened, a contingency that occurred with some regularity. The antennas were made up of two semi-circular rows of vertical dipoles arranged round the forward half of the conning tower, their patterns being swung electrically around 60°. This system was fitted into three operational boats, *U-156*, *U-157* and *U-158*, all Class IXC40 craft, employed in the East Asian theatre, but as may be imagined very little success attended this venture for the reasons given, and even when it worked, the maximum range was only about 7 km and in any case it had a restricted search radius depending on the direction of the boat at any time.

In 1942 a retractable rotating mast was developed which carried an array of dipoles against a reflector sheet of 1 by 1.4 metres, on the rear of which were mounted the two broadband dipoles *FuMB Ant. 5 Samoa* for the radio-detection system *W-Anz. g2 (FuMB 9) Cypern II*. During submersion this was retracted into a waterproof compartment on the side of the conning tower. Very little is now known about the effectiveness or otherwise of the system, but in late 1942 it was improved by including maximum direction-finding and it was re-classified as the *FMG 42 G (gU) (FuMO 30)*. This was built into all U-boats as standard equipment and though it may have proved of use in some operations it was easily rendered unserviceable by depth-charging or bombing. Most commanders refused to use it on the grounds that it betrayed their position (as many of them did) and as by now the British were hunting U-boats with all the means at their disposal only very short radar searches were possible. On top of this the effects of salt water on the antennas left much to be desired.

At this time the *FMG* classifications were replaced by the new *FuMO* designations, and new deliveries of the rotating columns for the (now) *FuMO 24* and *25* were fitted with slip-rings[1] so that the transmitter could be installed elsewhere in the boat's interior. This not only made rotation much easier but improved the speed and accuracy of direction-finding, yet at the same time it was found that the close resolution had deteriorated from 300 to 600 metres and this called for immediate measures. While this was being tackled a requirement was also made for some special installations for surface vessels. These included an additional equipment for the *Prinz Eugen*, the *FMG 40 G (FuMO 26)*, with extra antennas for locating aircraft, and a stanchion was also fitted to

---

[1] It is interesting to observe that this method had been employed by Hülsmeyer nearly forty years earlier.

the foremast to take the *FuMO 25* (qv), but due to the proximity of the mast its antennas could only rotate between 35 and 325°.

After the scuttling of the *Graf Spee* in December 1939 the High Command considered it wise to introduce the *Wismar* system to shipboard radar. From the reports of German sympathisers in South America it seemed evident that the British must have learned that the ship carried radar and jamming measures were only to be expected. But in the event, the earliest jamming of the coastal *Seetakts* only began in March 1941 and the Germans were mystified that the British should have taken so long to institute these countermeasures. They could not know that Bainbridge-Bell's report had remained ignored on a Whitehall shelf for well over a year, and even after the war when they learned the truth of the matter they found it hard to believe. In the meantime they 'scattered' the *Seetakt* frequencies so that it would operate between 330 and 430 MHz although at first this introduced problems with the antenna systems.

During this period the Navy also demanded stronger transmitters to increase the range and Gema came up with two models, the *Gisela* which delivered 125 kW and the *Gertrud* with 400 kW, both of which were spark transmitters to reduce the cost of valves and other components. The *Gisela* was provided with a rotating column for the antennas and proved fairly successful. Research into this model led to the development of the *FuMO 4 Seetakt* for coastal employment which used the platform of the *FuMO 2* and a larger horizontally polarised array of 3 by 6 metres. Since this gave very good service work was begun immediately on the *FuMO 5 Boulogne* (actually derived from the *Calais* system) with a 5 by 6.5 metre antenna, and for reducing its size and for ease of operation it was also equipped with a simpler measuring system. Echoes were displayed on an overall-view screen with a horizontal timebase line on which the ranges could be switched from 0 to 10 km, 1 to 15 km and 5 to 120 km, the calibration being effected through cross-fadable light points. Although relatively simple the equipment was quite successful and easy to manufacture since it used only 25 valves not including rectifiers.

Another equipment to utilise spark transmission was the 400 kW *Grete*, and it is known that a 1 megawatt version, the *Grete II*, was tested in Denmark, although little is now known about the results. It is however known that the 400 kW *Grete* was used for the development of a shipboard radar called the *FuMO 31*

Sophie which employed broadband dipoles on a 1 by 1.6 metre frame.[1] This operated in conjunction with a another system using A/N bearings, and the results were considered good enough for it to be used as the successor to the *FuMO 24* and *25*, but in February 1944 the idea was abandoned in favour of the *Hohentwiel* system.

The Navy also had control of land-based long-range radars on 80 cm which Gema began to produce in 1941. These included the *FMG 41 G (gA) (FuMO 51) Mammut-Gustav* on 368 MHz with 125 kW and a 200 kW version of the *FMG 41 G (cF) (FuMO 52) Mammut-Cäsar* operating between 187 and 220 MHz. A broadband design, the *FMG 42 G (cF) (FuMO 53) Mammut-Cäcilie*, was also used for fast direction-finding.

During a conference on 9 and 10 March 1943 the Navy expressed their concern that only a few firms were supplying their needs. Their displeasure was also directed at the delay and shortcomings of some of the equipment, despite the fact that it had been decreed that Luftwaffe equipment should be used where possible. As has been mentioned, a few *Würzburgs* had been pressed into service and, some time later, the *Hohentwiel* airborne radar was adapted and fitted with enlarged antennas for shipboard use. Lorenz, in particular, were ordered to prepare a large number of *Hohentwiels* for naval use and, after a while, the Navy actually got them. These included the *FuMO 61 Hohentwiel U* with a 1 by 1.4 metre rotating antenna for U-boats, the *FuMO 62 Hohentwiel S* for patrol boats with a 1.5 by 1.6 metre antenna, the *FuMO 63 Hohentwiel K* designed for torpedo boats with a 2 by 2.4 metre antenna, and sometimes employed in destroyers and light cruisers, and the *FuMO 64 Hohentwiel-Lang* built on a *Chinese* rotating platform with a 2 by 8 metre rotating array for use in coastal defence.

Another model, the *FuMO 65 Hohentwiel U1*, was also designed for U-boats and had a 1 by 1.4 metre rotating antenna. This could be simultaneously switched to sector or panoramic scanning as desired. Of these radars all were horizontally polarised except the *FuMO 61, 62* and *65*. The *FuMO 61*, having the smallest antenna and the lowest operating

[1] Compared to Hülsmeyer's equipment this spark transmitter was hundreds of times more powerful and delivered its energy to unscreened antennas. The operating frequencies between 330 and 430 MHz being lower than Hülsmeyer's 600 MHz (50 cm) called for longer antennas in any case, and obviously the receiver muting was more sophisticated. Yet at no time from any source was the complaint heard that extraneous radiations and returns from the ship's upperworks would have rendered it useless.

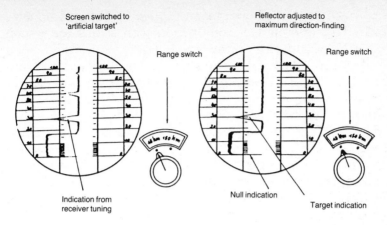

Screen switched to 'artificial target'

Reflector adjusted to maximum direction-finding

Range switch

Range switch

Indication from receiver tuning

Null indication

Target indication

Figure 38 The range measurement principle of the *FuMO 61 Hohentweil U* (*Fritz Trenkle*).

height, had a range of only 10 km against ships and about 20 km for aircraft; the rest with their larger arrays and greater working heights had about double the range, that of the *FuMO 64* being about 36 km against medium size ships. All of them were fairly simple equipments with only 19 valves, but they were very reliable and easy to maintain. Designed for maximum direction-finding with an accuracy of 3° the range indication could be switched between 0 to 10 km and 0 to 100 km, but this was later changed to 0 to 15 km and 0 to 150 km, the shorter ranges having an accuracy of about 100 metres.

The *FuMO 65* was provided with the PPI screen *Drauf* and it was believed (unfortunately without foundation) that its orbital sweep furnished the monitoring enemy with only a very brief pulse of radiation at a given point, thus making it difficult for him to get a quick bearing. This particular radar was only used in a few Class XXI boats for a short time before it was replaced by later models, but naval personnel spoke highly of its usefulness in coastal waters especially where pilotage at night was difficult.

The E-boats now called for attention, and Gema designed a lightweight radar based on the ASV *Rostock* on 125 MHz with 1.5 kW of power, but the antennas were too large for such a small craft and surface reflections from the boat gave a great deal of trouble. But by the end of 1943 when the Luftwaffe's *Lichtenstein B/C* had been replaced by improved models, the Navy promptly took it over and adapted it to their own requirements. As it worked on much higher frequencies and used correspondingly smaller antennas, plus the fact that they expected very little enemy jamming, it seemed to hold some promise. Accordingly, it was re-designed and re-classified as the *FuMO 71 Lichtenstein B/C*. The height-finding screen was removed (since surface vessels do not aspire to great altitudes) and the number of valves reduced to 31. With 1.5 kW on 476 MHz it gave a range of about 2 km against destroyers and similar size vessels, but owing to the fixed position of the antennas the forward beamwidth of only 35° meant that the boat had to make a series of circular sweeps to cover a wide area. In practice it was mostly used in line-of-sight operation when ranges of up to 6 km against large ships were usual.

To overcome this limitation a rotating antenna was built against a reflector of 1.3 by 1.6 metres and much was expected of it, but during active service it merely served to enlarge the reflecting area of the boat's surface to the extent where it was more easily located by the enemy, and after several weeks of successful gunnery by the British the system was given the nickname *Seezielgranatensammelkasten*, or literally, 'See Target Shell Collecting Box'.

The idea was also tried out later in patrol boats, particularly the *VP* (*Vorpostenboot*) *1107*, but this merely provided an even larger reflecting surface with similar results. In fact, only three of these systems were ever seriously employed and a new version, the *Lichtenstein U* for U-boats, was never introduced.

In March 1944 the E-Boats again clamoured for help and a variation of the *Hohentwiel* was tried out, but again surface reflections from the craft resulted in the same treatment from the British.

In the middle of 1944 9 cm radars were made available to the Navy, most of them based on the Luftwaffe's *FuG 224 Berlin A*. These were designed by Telefunken and used the platform of the *Calais* equipment on which was mounted a 3 metre diameter parabolic reflector from the *Würzburg A* fitted with a *Berlin* antenna, the transmitter and receiver being built into a waterproof casing immediately behind the reflector. This equipment was called the *FuMO 11 Renner I* (Winner or World-beater) and employed maximum direction-finding with a prf of 500 Hz to give a range of 32 km against small ships and up to 70 km against larger ones. A much improved second version, the *FuMO 12 Renner II*, used the PPI screen *Drauf*, and its successor, *FuMO 13 Renner III*, differed in having its reflector mounted on a tall rotating column similar to those employed in bunkers.

To what extent these were successful as sector or panoramic

radars is not known, but some merit must have been found in them because Telefunken used the basic design for another coastal equipment called the *FuMO 14 Berlin L*. The *Renner I* was also used by Telefunken as the basis of the *FuMO 15 Scheer* and this model is known to have been very successful. It incorporated the *Berlin* equipment with the platform and reflector of the *Würzburg Riese* and employed maximum direction-finding with the PPI screen *Drauf*, the antenna rotation being about 4 rpm. With this radar the tops of masts could be located from coastal positions at ranges up to 70 km.

The use of 9 cm radar for coastal use was a great boon to the naval defence organisation, but it could only be produced in very small numbers. In March 1945 only 29 were in use on the North Sea coast between Holland and Norway, 8 in the Baltic and 6 in the Mediterranean.

As may be imagined, Telefunken's 9 cm equipment placed them in a very leading position in the field of radar and Gema, as mentioned, were obliged to co-operate with them for much of the time after 1943. A joint development, of which great things were expected, was the *FuMO 41 Segler I* (Yachtsman or sailor) intended for shipboard use. This employed most of the components of the *Berlin* system in a small case designed for fixing to a ship's mast with Yagi antennas arranged in a 0.6 by 3 metre paraboloid segment mounted above it. Tests proved this to be very useful but for some reason it never went into service.

A very successful shipboard system was the *FuMO 81 Berlin S*. Ranges up to 30 km against small ships were recorded with a close resolution of about 1 km and a range accuracy of about 100 metres, but the direction-finding accuracy of only 5° was considered not good enough. After further experimentation this was improved to 0.5°, and although the PPI screen *Drauf* was used it also employed a standard screen with a horizontal timebase line which, in conjunction with the mechanical computer *X-Uhr*, also enabled the system to be used for torpedo aiming. The antennas were four ceramic stubs mounted horizontally on a motor-driven disc which also delivered the voltage for the screen's deflection plates over a two-phase generator, the entire system being enclosed in a metal and Plexiglass radome. From 1944 up to the end of the war this radar was employed in many different types of ships from E-boats up to the *Prinz Eugen*. It proved itself to a remarkable degree during the retreat from the Russian advance in the Baltic when an E-boat fitted with it led over a hundred smaller vessels crammed with over 20,000 refugees, by night and under gunfire, through a gap in a minefield only 100 metres wide, the buoys marking its edge being easily detected.

Its successor, the *FuMO 82 Berlin K*, was designed as a panoramic radar for big ships and thus employed larger antennas. These used combinations of between six and eight ceramic stubs, and an idea having been suggested that these might be used for U-boats, Elac designed pressurised casings for them with a number of ceramic apertures. Much thought was given to the design of these antennas, which received the code-name *Bullauge* (Bullseye, or perhaps more appropriately, Porthole) but in the event they proved too heavy for use. More success came with the following model, the *FuMO 83 Berlin U1*, which employed only four ceramic stubs mounted in a plastic sphere on top of a rotating mast, and could be used either for maximum direction-finding or panoramic scanning as required. A U-boat skipper chosen to test the system reported that he had a view similar to 'what might be seen from a balloon 200 metres above the boat', fine details of shipping, anchorages and buildings being faithfully portrayed. A final version, the *FuMO 84 Berlin U II*, was.based on its predecessor but did not use a retractable mast, and despite a great deal of research it never went into production although it was occasionally used as an experimental model. The same fate overtook the *Berlin E* which had 5 kW of power, and the 1.5 cm *Berlin D*, although both equipments performed very well under test conditions.

For the purposes of naval gunnery it had been realised long before the war that an improved range measurement accuracy of at least 80 metres and a bearing accuracy of about $0.25°$ would be required. For these reasons experiments were carried out with the *FuMO 101*, a model derived from the *FuMO 3 Calais-Zerstörersäule*, which now had a 3 by 6 metre horizontally polarised antenna and mechanical direction-finding, but these tests proved that larger antennas had to be employed and successive models were designed for antennas up to 10 by 10 metres. These were built on the rotating platform of the *Freya LZ* and given the classifications *Dünkirchen g*, which operated between 330 and 430 MHz with 400 kW of power, and the *Dünkirchen c* which delivered 1 megawatt between 180 and 250 MHz. Both of these equipments were designed and built by Gema in co-operation with the Communications Research Establishment, and some of them saw service in France.

In 1943 personnel in some of the naval coastal batteries

became acquainted with members of the neighbouring Luftwaffe (Flak) installations and in particular with the Flak's *Würzburg Riese*. This seemed such a superior radar to their own that they made a request for it which, surprisingly enough, was granted. But shortly after receiving a few sets their opinion fell sharply. The main problem was that, as mentioned, the Navy had very few skilled personnel to maintain this sensitive equipment and as a result the bearing accuracy began to fall off. Storms and salt water led to corrosion, and on top of this the blast of the heavier naval guns often put it out of action. The Navy also suffered due to their rather poor relations with the Observer Corps. In many instances their only communication with each other was by telephone, and as the lines did not always receive skilled maintenance crossed lines and breakdowns were commonplace.

Efforts to assist naval gunnery continued with an adaptation of the *FuMO 15 Scheer*, also known as the *FuMO III Barbara I*. This also used the components of the *Berlin* system and was mounted on the platform of the *Würzburg Riese*, the *Quirl* being replaced by the *Zenti-Grille* antenna. A great deal of time was spent in making this equipment as robust as possible for naval requirements, and from reports it seems that it found favour with the Gunnery Officers as it not only stood up very well to the blasts of salvoes but was very easy to maintain. Above all, its accuracy was so good that the fall of shot could easily be determined and very few corrections were needed for a straddle. The only problem was that the focusing was so fine that for speedy target location a lower frequency would be better, something similar to the *Würzburg Riese*'s, so another model was designed using this lower frequency and was given the improved display unit from the *Euklid* system which now included a PPI screen. This was known as the *Barbara II* and was much appreciated by the gunners because it could work in a number of modes. It could perform either as a straight search radar or for sector-panoramic use, and it was equally useful as a panoramic scanner. And to combat enemy jamming the high-frequency components were easily interchangeable with those of the *Seetakt* or *Euklid* radars. A successor to this known as the *Barbara D* on 3 cm is known to have been planned but further details are no longer available.

An interesting project of this time, about which, unfortunately, few details remain, was a design by Professor Kohl of the Communications Research Station at Pelzerhaken. This employed the components of the *Berlin* system and the

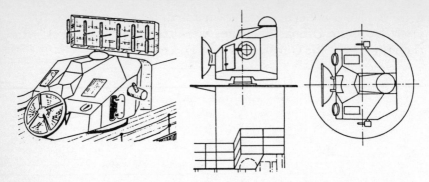

Figure 39 Three views of the shipboard Flak radar *FuMO 231 Euklid* with additional IFF antennae (125 to 156 MHz) on the left (*Fritz Trenkle*).

reflector of the *Würzburg Riese* in a circuit which generated a series of scanning signals together with a line-blanking method to produce what he called a Radio-Vision System which gave a picture similar to a television set. While no details of the range are known, it is believed that during tests it clearly portrayed, amongst other details, a lifeboat being lowered from a ship. A similar system was also designed by Dr Stützer of the FFO, but again no details are known.

Towards the end of the war Telefunken designed a shipboard gunnery radar called the *Segler II* but the pressures of war did not allow this to go into service. It used the *Berlin* radar and segments of the reflectors of both the *Würzburg A* and the *Würzburg Riese* with the *Zenti-Grille* dipole. At the same time the *Ballspiel* (Ball game) general search and gunnery radar was produced. Intended for U-boat employment it had an overall range of 25 km, although for gunnery purposes it was only used up to 8 km, with a direction-finding accuracy of about 1° and a close resolution of 500 metres. While this is known to have seen active service its results are no longer known, as is the case with another design called *Seerose* (Water Lily) by Dr Kluge of Telefunken. This was intended for surface ships and had its foundation in the *Berlin* radar, using a new display unit with a special angle-determining equipment known as *Seebär* (Fur Seal).

To conclude, it should be pointed out that while this chapter has dealt with the most prominent types of naval radar, it by no means follows that the systems mentioned constitute the entire range. In many cases radars designed for other services and for quite different applications were often adapted and used for a particular need at any time. It is also only fair to say that while the Navy through its research establishments did more in the early days to put German radar on a firm footing, it is clear that apart from the U-boat Arm they were treated with less regard than the rest of the German Armed Forces.

CHAPTER ELEVEN

Fighter-Guidance Radar

Before the war no fighter-guidance system was envisaged in Germany. As mentioned, the military philosophy was one of striking-power rather than defence, although in 1937 a handful of strategists began to think otherwise, but even then it was believed all that was necessary were a few flak guns, a string of sound locators and the eyes of the Observer Corps. Sometimes an occasional fighter might take off and fly a patrol, but even by 1938 rarely more than two or three aircraft performed this duty, since the prevailing attitude was summed up in the motto: 'The Luftwaffe attacks but does not defend.' And of course most people were happy to believe Göring's declaration that Germany would never be bombed.

By December 1939, several weeks after the RAF had made their presence felt over the German harbours, it began to dawn on them that a system of directing fighters to enemy aircraft might, after all, be desirable, and this view was certainly shared by Kammhuber and Leutnant Diehl, the latter's work with the *Freya* on Wangerooge having been already discussed, but even then it was not until 17 July 1940 that Kammhuber was permitted to form the first nightfighting Group, and this was employed in two different tactics. The first scheme was known as the Close Nightfighter Belt, but this name was soon changed to the Illuminated Belt, which was an area flooded by searchlights, sound locators and the Observer Corps, from Schleswig-Holstein, over Hamburg, Bremen and the Ruhr, right up to Metz. After being alerted by the Observer Corps, a single nightfighter took off and patrolled an area round a radio beacon. At the same time twin searchlights scanned the sky for the enemy, and if successful, they held it in a so-called *Lichtdom*

(Cathedral of light) so that the fighter could attack it. But from the very start this idea was difficult in practice due to the fog and smut over the industrial regions. By October the *Würzburg A* had replaced the sound locators, and while this was very successful, the limitations of the Illuminated Belt itself became obvious because its 35 kilometre width could be easily avoided by enemy aircraft which either by-passed it or merely flew at greater heights.

Kammhuber's second tactic was the employment of the Long-Distance Nightfighter. This idea was tested with two squadrons of Ju88 and Do17 aircraft, the principle being to follow British bombers returning home and to shoot them down as they landed. These original 'intruders' were quite successful, but their sorties were stopped by Hitler for propaganda reasons, i.e. 'kills' were hard to substantiate over England and the German public demanded proof.[1]

On 17 September Diehl, with Martini's support, installed *Freyas* on the southern side of the Zuider Zee. The accuracy now having been much improved by the introduction of A/N bearings, the echoes could be displayed together with a map grid superimposed on the screen so that the courses of the enemy and the pursuing fighter could be seen simultaneously. On the night of 16 October the system had its first success when two British aircraft were shot down, but it was subsequently found that the height-finding circuits were faulty, and it was not until these were put in order that the system proved to be of value. A string of these radars was soon working very effectively in what Diehl called the Dark Belt, many aircraft being caught in it before reaching Kammhuber's Illuminated Belt.

During the same month Diehl introduced his *Scheinwerfer-Parasit* (Searchlight parasite), which was an arrangement of four *Freya* dipoles mounted on searchlights, the output being fed to a display unit where the resulting traces were compared to those from a standard *Freya* in the neighbourhood, and enabled the searchlights to be directed more accurately and speedily.

By now it had become very obvious to the High Command

---

[1] From the German military viewpoint Hitler's intervention was hasty and ill-considered. These 'intruders' were ordered to the Mediterranean theatre instead, but when the real value of their operations was finally realised they were restarted over England in August 1943, but by then the British defences were ready.

that an effective nightfighting system was needed and the Air Defence Command set up a combined nightfighting system over nine industrial cities made up of three sectors each containing a *Freya* and two *Würzburgs*, around which a nightfighter made an orbit. The coarse location of the enemy was determined by the *Freya*, aided by one of the *Würzburgs* for finer pin-pointing, while the other *Würzburg* tracked the fighter and guided it to the target. Plotting was carried out in the ground control station by means of narrow beams of red and blue light from special projectors on to a ground glass screen on which was superimposed a detailed map of the area, the operation of the beams being undertaken by personnel on the reception of data from the radar positions. The Ground Control Officer, knowing the position of his Flak and searchlight batteries, could then tell his Divisional Commander over radio-telephony the enemy's course should the fighter have failed to find its target. But although the idea was sound in principle it was not very good in practice and a different method had to be considered.

This need was more pronounced by the summer of 1941 when the German divisions began their onslaught against the Soviet Union and the British bomber offensive grew correspondingly heavier. To meet it a system was designed with the name of *Uhu*, and this was used in conjunction with a special receiver called the *Fu28a* which was installed in nightfighters mainly at Leeuwarden in Holland. The transmitter accompanying this project was the *Berta 1 II* together with the beam system *FuSan 723 Wotan*, both using a common omni-directional antenna to receive the respective beam directions of the ground transmitter and those from the aircraft, thus enabling bearings to be found very quickly. And not only could the bearings of both enemy and fighter be determined, but by varying the degree of modulation of another carrier the fighter received a left-right indication in the cockpit which enabled it to track the centre of the beam and thus be directed to its target. The ground transmitter could be switched off at any time to permit courses to be given over radio-telephony if required. But again, while sound in theory, the system was not only complicated but had two major drawbacks. The pilots were understandably very reluctant to have their aircraft controls virtually dictated from the ground, but more importantly, the system could not distinguish between friend and foe.

This latter weakness had of course been recognised from the

beginning, for while *Uhu* was in operation Rechlin were testing Gema's IFF system, the *FuG 25a Erstling*, and it occurred to them that it might very well be used for fighter guidance by employing it in conjunction with a pair of *Freyas*, one of which would track the fighter and the other the enemy, while A/N bearings could be used to plot the respective positions, the fighter being recognised of course by the IFF signals from its *Erstling*. In fact, the *Erstling* system could be used on its own, the principal difference being that the *Erstling* method required a plotting table and with the A/N system of the *Freyas* the pilots were dependent on the instructions from its operators. If the pilots' prejudice against the latter idea could have been overcome it would, in fact, have made a very good system because the *Freya*'s wide-angle pattern of about 40° would enable any fighter in its sector to be given a course by the operators without the need for a map.

At about the same time another fighter guidance system was introduced which was based on a British device. During the Battle of Britain the British fighters were assisted by what was called the *Pip-Squeak* system whereby the leader of their flights transmitted a time-switch controlled signal at the end of every few minutes, thus enabling their ground control to establish their position through triangulation, and also making it easy for the enemy aircraft already detected by radar to be pin-pointed.

Rechlin discussed this method at some length, and after some research had been carried out a similar idea was introduced called the Direction-Finding-Call-System which, despite the opposition of many pilots, was eventually installed in several fighters. The scheme used time switches and tone modulation on much the same lines as the British method, and was used in conjunction with the short wave Adcock Direction-Finding System *Fu-Peil A 70*. But although this showed promise more research was needed, and it was left to Dr Troost of Telefunken to improve it by combining it with the French receiver *R87C Sadir* to produce what was called the *Fu-Peil 80 Tornado*. At the end of every two minutes the Flight Leader transmitted an automatically-keyed morse signal over a time-switch which was received at three ground stations and fed to a plotting table on which the three points of intersection were displayed. During periods of direction-finding the radio-telephony link was interrupted to allow the direction-finding equipment to change frequency if required. But promising as the system seemed during tests it was virtually useless on short waves and it was not until a similar system was devised for UHF operation that any success was obtained.

In October 1941 Kammhuber approached Plendl at Rechlin to enquire whether the *Y-E (Freya-Würzburg)* radar system could be used in conjunction with the fighter radio-telephony system *FuG 16 Z* for the guidance of day fighters. Plendl thought it was possible and put the research for this in the hands of Leutnant (later Dr) Schaeder. Under Schaeder's direction the *FuG 16 Z* was vastly improved and combined with a ground installation called *Wotan III* and the VHF direction-finding system *Heinrich* to produce what was called the *Y-System* for day fighters. (This was also used for blind bombing.) At the end of every 20 minutes the *Wotan* sent out a signal of 5 minutes' duration modulated by a range-measurement tone independent of the radio-telephony link on the same frequency.

The signal was picked up by the Flight Leader and re-transmitted on 1.9 MHz, thus enabling the aircraft's range to be determined, while its bearings were ascertained by the *Heinrich* system. As all fighters used the same radio-telephony frequency as the ground installation intercommunication was of course possible, a number of frequencies being available if required. At the plotting table the positions of fighters and enemy aircraft could be displayed and the appropriate courses given. But again, though promising in theory the system failed to give the expected results when it was tested by the Luftwaffe Research Regiment at Oldenburg. The frequencies chosen were, it seems, only optimal for combat operations at certain heights and for this reason had to be changed.

While more research into this was being carried out Kammhuber decided to re-organise the nightfighter scheme. As mentioned, one of the weaknesses of the Illuminated Belt was its narrow width which permitted enemy aircraft to avoid it. Another problem was that the pursuing fighter was obliged to break off the action at the border of its own sector and hand over the enemy to the next one. Kammhuber's solution called for the provision of two *Würzburg Riesen*, a *Freya*, and a much improved plotting method known as the *Seeburg Tisch*. And since the *Lichtenstein BC* was now installed in several fighters it was relatively easy to direct them by radio-telephony in Diehl's Dark Belt until any enemy who had been lucky enough to evade the Illuminated Belt could be detected by the *Lichtenstein*-equipped fighter and hopefully shot down. This combination of the Dark and Illuminated Belts and their accompanying equipments soon produced good results and was known as the *Seeburg-Lichtenstein-System*[1].

It should perhaps be mentioned that although this system still called for much work and organisation in its early stages, it nevertheless accounted for the destruction of over 120 British aircraft. Yet it still failed to come up to expectations. This led in early 1942 to a somewhat heated discussion at Rechlin about the merits of other systems and it was decided to try a development using a combination of the *Erstling* and the *Y-System*, but due to the heavy commitments of industry to other war work its production was slow. This goaded Kammhuber into greater activity and he immediately ordered a complete revision of the *Seeburg-Lichtenstein-System* and the introduction of a much more sophisticated method of fighter guidance. This was the *Himmelbett System* (Four-poster bed system) which proved so successful that a number of searchlight companies could now be withdrawn from the Illuminated Belt for the defence of individual cities. This left an extended Dark Belt known as *Dunaja*,[2] which was made up of a series of sectors or 'boxes' each containing 2 *Freyas*, 2 *Würzburg Riesen*, 1 *Seeburg Tisch*, 1 VHF ground-to-air transceiver, 1 (or 2) 100 watt medium-wave beacons and a light beacon.

After tests in different regions and a modification of some frequencies the system went into service between April and May 1943 in a line stretching from the Dutch coast to the Ruhr. Long-range surveillance radars such as *Wassermann* or *Mammut* gave warning of an impending raid, upon which the fighters were scrambled to orbit the medium-wave beacon or, when fitted, the light beacon, and the Leader was directed to the enemy by radio-telephony after the courses of both enemy and fighter had been plotted first by the *Freyas* and then by the *Würzburgs*. Up to this point the system still worked like the *Seeburg-Lichtenstein-System* but differed now in frequencies, operation and material. The *Seeburg Tisch*, for example was much improved, and though one *Würzburg* still tracked the enemy and the other directed the fighter as before, and their respective positions were still indicated on the *Seeburg Tisch* by thinly projected coloured beams (red for the enemy and blue

---

[1] Not to be confused with the *Himmelbett System* which was derived from it but came later.

[2] *Dunaja* is a contraction of *Dunkel Nachtjagd* (Dark night-fighting), similarly *Henaja* (not mentioned in the text) stood for *Helle Nachtjagd* or Bright night-fighting = the Illuminated Belt.

for the fighter) the accuracy was greatly improved, as was the communication link between the operators at the Table and the radar personnel.

The chief improvement was, however, that now more than one fighter could be directed at any time and identification of individual fighters was accurately and speedily achieved. And although the fighters still had to break off the action at the limits of their own 'box', the hand-over to the next one was much quicker. The biggest problem was that it required at least 140 ground operators for one fighter to be directed to its target, but nevertheless it gave very good results over a long period until the RAF began their 1,000 bomber raids when it became almost useless. It was also particularly susceptible to jamming by *Window*.

In October 1942 the 'Railway Radars' or the Railway Air Signals Companies were formed from the Signals Regiment (E) V21 under the command of Major Bury, originally of the Second Corps of Air Signals Regiment 42, and later succeeded by Major W. Bode. The task of these railway companies ranged from radar reporting (early warning) to nightfighter guidance, and they were mainly employed to fill the gaps in the defence system against Russian attacks.

The average train consisted of four low-loader wagons, two of which carried a pair of *Würzburg Riesen* while two more were mounted with *Freyas*. Twenty-two items of rolling stock were utilised, consisting of eight passenger coaches for the accommodation of two officers, 25 NCO's and about 100 other ranks. The additional wagons carried the evaluation and plotting equipment, the radio-telephone links using the *FuG 10* and *FuG 16* receivers, an orderly room, canteen and sickbay. A further wagon carried a lorry, a Volkswagen cross-country runabout, a motorcycle and spare parts.

The radio installation included a ground-to-air R/T link, a data-transmission system to a permanent plotting station, a radio-telephone connection to Headquarters, and a radio or telephone link to the nearest Army Command Post.

According to the particular tract of country the equipment could either be used from the train or on gun-carriages, the assembling of the equipment in the latter case taking about nine hours, though dismantling was easier at only four hours. The erection of protective screening and camouflage was also a time-consuming feature. For defence against air or ground attack every train was equipped with two 4-barrelled 2 cm Flak guns, a number of machine guns and often the 98K heavy machine gun. The defence crew went into action on receipt of the command-word *Feuerzauber* (Magic fire).

Three companies were employed in these 'Railway Radar Units' and came under the general command of *XII Fliegerkorps*. For their early-warning tasks they were designated 'Sumatra I, II and III' ('Sumatra' standing for *suchen*, to search) and for fighter guidance the codename 'Java' (from *jagen*, to hunt) was employed.

These companies gave very good accounts of themselves on the eastern front. At one time companies of the Signals Regiment *Raubvögel* (Bird of prey) defended the Hermann-Göring Werke near Salzgitter quite successfully, and four such trains were used in 1944 at Brest-Litovsk and later at Baranov-Brückenkopf where they worked in co-operation with the First Nightfighter Group 100. Two of the companies were lost in Bulgaria in August 1944 after performing sterling work.

*

The British of course were well aware that the Germans had instituted a new form of fighter guidance. Not only had bomber crews reported the absence of searchlights over certain areas, but the presence of nightfighters in these dark regions clearly pointed to some form of radar control. It was obviously necessary to send specially equipped aircraft on sorties to pin-point these radar installations and find their frequencies. Radar specialists from TRE volunteered as observers and were given RAF commissions in case they fell into enemy hands. Among these was Howard Cundall who had to bale out over France and despite a brave effort to row back to England in a boat he had seized on the coast, was captured and sent to *Stalag Luft III*, where he immediately built a radio transmitter and sent London a great deal of useful information.[1]

Another observer was Eric Ackermann who in two years made over 90 flights in which he recorded the *Würzburg* transmissions very frequently.

Besides the radar transmissions the British could monitor the German radio-telephony traffic between their ground control and the fighters when frequent reference to something called *Kleine-Schraube* (Little screw) was heard. It did not take Jones

---

[1] Again, this is what Jones was told at the time, and in Cundall's obituary in *The Times* the building of the transmitter was mentioned. However James Langley and M.R.D. Foot in their book *MI9 Escape and Evasion* could find no evidence that the transmitter had been either built or used.

long to realise this was the codeword for the radio beacon the nightfighter had to orbit. (Both sides could at times be ridiculously informative with codewords.) And by now it was obvious that the Germans were employing a defensive strip split into a number of sections each equipped with a number of radars and plotting stations, all of which according to agents' reports and de-coded radio traffic were commanded by a General Kammhuber. And since Jones wanted a name to put to this system he immediately christened it the *Kammhuber Line*, to Kammhuber's rueful amusement after the war.

Possibly the greatest contribution to the discovery of the *Kammhuber Line* and the *Himmelbett System* was made by a member of the Belgian Resistance who, having been requested to make a survey of all the sectors in his region and feeling daunted by the prospect of a long cycling trip around the countryside, thought it easier to break into the headquarters of a nearby regimental commander and steal his maps, which he promptly did. From these Jones and his team were able to piece together the entire working method of the system and advise Air Chief Marshal 'Bomber' Harris of the appropriate countermeasures.

Because the *Würzburg* and *Lichtenstein* frequencies lay fairly close to each other the *Himmelbett System* received a severe blow when the Allies dropped *Window* on the night of the Hamburg Raid. This and similar attacks by night and day so disrupted the system that Kammhuber was relieved of his post and replaced by General 'Beppo' Schmid who ordered immediate countermeasures including the employment of a system using Major Herrmann's forward-striking nightfighters known as the *Wilde-Sau-Verfahren* (Wild Sow system).[1] This had in fact been devised much earlier but the limited research into it left much to be desired, particularly as the single-seater fighters employed carried no radar but depended on searchlights or parachute flares to find their targets. Nevertheless the system

---

[1] Strictly speaking this was less a 'forward-striking' system of nightfighting than an offensive use of single-seat single-engined *day* fighters at night, guided by searchlights and other light signals. Nearly all *Wilde Sau* pilots, who were volunteers, flew *borrowed dayfighter* aircraft, which was one of the main drawbacks of this otherwise quite successful tactic. Time and again the *Wilde Sau* pilots had to make forced landings, 'bending' their borrowed fighters, to the understandable chagrin of their rightful owners. Apart from that, the lighting-up effort needed to make the system work (special 'illuminator' aircraft, coloured searchlights and other light signals) confused the other nightfighter crews and the ground defences, and was really too complicated and wasteful to continue.

had some success, especially when enemy bombers were thrown into relief by the ground fires they had themselves started. On the debit side, the training of pilots and observers in the use of the new nightfighter radars such as the *FuG 217* and *218 Neptun* and the *FuG 220 Lichtenstein SN2* was seriously held up by the need to employ almost every aircraft for Herrmann's system.

The Hamburg Raid was followed up the following night by a similar attack on Essen, and as this city was better placed for the British to monitor the radio-telephony traffic, Jones and his team had an excellent opportunity to learn how the Germans were dealing with the situation.

> The Essen raid started normally enough. One of our bombers was shot down a minute after midnight, presumably an early casualty unprotected by *Window*, since the first aircraft in a smokescreen must always be vulnerable. But soon we heard the ground controls in various stages of perplexity, not only in trying to follow our bombers but also their own fighters. One control lost his fighter for eighteen minutes, repeatedly asking him to make the identifying right-left wing waggle (*Rolf-Lise*) which should have caused his radar echo to wax and wane. I heard the controller getting more and more exasperated, presumably because his Giant *Würzburg* had fixed on a packet of *Window* instead of the fighter. Even his most stentorian '*Rolf-Lise machen!*' produced no response from the *Window*, while another controller told his aircraft 'break off, the bombers are multiplying themselves'. A fighter complained that his control could not even tell him whether the bombers were coming from the north or the south. All these fragments indicated that the Kammhuber system was substantially disrupted; and this was reflected in our casualties, which, although substantially greater than those on Hamburg, were still only 23 out of 705 aircraft or 3.3%.

Simultaneously with Herrmann's fighters those of Oberst Viktor von Lossberg, Milch's nightfighter specialist, were also employed in what was called the Constant-Maintaining-System. This called for the replacement of the *FuG 16 Z* with an improved version, the *FuG 16 YZ*, so that every fighter group could be guided by a 'contact-keeping' leader over the *Y-System* which in turn was dependent upon the data from the coastal radars. The leader and his group, together with the ground installations, all used the same set of frequencies and the ground controller gave the necessary course directions as before, but now the principle of attack was that the fighters should approach at such a height or position where they would not be affected by *Window*. They also had to be sure and not to attack from behind where they would be detected by the enemy's rear-warning radar.

By October 1943 this system was developed into the *Nachtaufklärer System* (Nightscout system) and was given nicknames such as *Salvator* or *Beppo*. Its purpose was to detect enemy bombers fitted with H_2S and report their positions to the ground whereupon other fighters were directed to them. The Ju88G was mainly used for this purpose and equipped with the *Lichtenstein SN2*, the passive homing system *FuG 227 Flensburg* for detecting the British *Monica* rear-warning radar, and the *FuG 350 Z Naxos Z* for H_2S.

This method was used up to May 1944 when it was withdrawn in favour of a return to more orthodox fighter tactics. To assist in these occasional use was made of the older *Knickebein* blind-bombing system, now code-named *Ottokar*, which was intended to locate aircraft by using frequencies around 30 MHz, but the idea was not successful. In any event a return was made to the *Nachtaufklärer* system later that year after all German airborne radar had been subjected to very strong jamming and all but crippled by masses of *Window* dropped by special flights over selected areas. At the same time the Allies used a number of deception techniques to lure the fighters away from the main bomber streams, chief among them being the use of H_2S and *Monica* signals by a few chosen aircraft while the main streams made little or no use of them. This puzzled the Germans for a while until they discovered the British had found their detection equipment in a crashed German aircraft and were putting it to good use.

By now von Lossberg had developed another method known officially as the *Verfolgungs-Nachtjagd-Verfahren* (Nightfighter Pursuit System), more commonly referred to as the *Zahme-Sau* (Tame sow) System. This called for the entire services of the *Himmelbett* System and practically every other radio-navigational aid. The idea was that the fighters should scramble and orbit one of the beacons in the predicted path of the raid and then engage the enemy as he approached instead of waiting until he was nearly overhead. It also meant a partial return to the old 'independent fighter' method but with radio-navigational guidance over long stretches. The idea certainly seemed promising, especially with the new He219 and the Ju88R and guidance was often carried out by either the *Ottokar* or a new method called the *Zyklopfeuer* system. These however were only useful when the fighters flew in formation (which was rare) as only the leader himself could be guided.

The situation grew so desperate that it reached the stage where nearly every transmitting system in Germany was pressed into service, including long-wave, medium-wave and short-wave broadcasting stations and a large number of beacon lights, but by now the Allied bombing was so intense that these measures were virtually ineffective. The *Y-System* direction-finding antennas mounted on towers were a special target for Allied fighter-bombers and in a last-ditch attempt to counteract this a system was quickly designed by Dr Zisler at Rechlin, in co-operation with the FFO, called the *Schildkröten-Peiler* (Turtle Direction-Finder). This was a method whereby the equipment was concealed under a camouflage net and, in fact, proved quite useful. And at the same time Lorenz designed what was called the Interference Blanking System which was also very effective. But despite all-out efforts on the part of the industry Allied bombing had taken so heavy a toll that never enough sets of either system could be supplied. Even during the last few days of the war Schmid thought that the few nightfighters left at his disposal might have better prospects if a large number of panoramic scanning radars could be made available, but by then the damage to the industry was mortal and further large-scale help was impossible. The final curtain was coming down ever faster and inexorably on the drama of war.

*

Of all the Allied countermeasures against German radar the employment of *Window* was probably the most effective. The confusion amongst the German ground controllers was particularly noticeable towards the end of 1943 and this often led to periods of amusement on the part of the British monitoring stations. Jones, who had returned from a short leave in September 1943, went down to the monitoring station at Kingsdown where, on the night of 29 September, it was clear that the German controller had convinced himself that a raid on Bochum in the Ruhr was really intended for Bremen, and was in fact telling his nightfighters so. On 4 October Jones wrote a report:

The present German system is unstable in that once the

controller has formed a picture of the situation it becomes increasingly easy for him to convince himself that he is right. Having made his guess at the target from the early track of the bombers, he sends his fighters to a convenient beacon. These fighters are then reported by sound observations and, unless the observers are extremely skilled, they may easily be misidentified. The controller then interprets the observations as referring to British aircraft, and is thus confirmed in his initial misjudgement, and so may order up more fighters which again may be misidentified. At Bremen the self-deception went even further; the flak opened fire, possibly delighted by the absence of *Window*, and at least one fighter dropped a flare presumably to illuminate our bombers which were in fact at Bochum, 150 miles away. The flare probably convinced the JD2 controller that the Pathfinders had arrived for even when JD1 announced that bombs were falling at Bochum, JD2 countermanded the JD1 order for the fighters to concentrate on Bochum.

Oddly enough, the same situation often prevailed in daytime. But at night, when the controller's confusion grew too great, British listeners would often hear the lines being cleared for take-over by a higher command and they sometimes wondered just how high this command was. Clarification came later in Adolf Galland's book *The First and the Last*, when it appeared that during a daylight raid by the Americans on Düren in the Rhineland, when a large quantity of *Window* was dropped, Göring himself took over control and assumed that because the *Window* cloud was drifting to the east, the Americans were about to attack Schweinfurt. The fighters sent up reported no enemy aircraft over Schweinfurt but a report promptly came from the ground observers that the enemy himself was then over Schweinfurt. Göring then decided that the enemy was heading for Leipzig, where the same thing happened again, causing him to conclude that the enemy were really making for the Skoda works near Pilsen in Czechoslovakia, but over Pilsen the air was clear and no aircraft were seen except some German fighters.

It was obvious to the whole fighter organisation that Göring had literally taken them for a ride, which he had the sense of humour to acknowledge by sending out a signal congratulating himself and all participants on the 'successful defeat of the air-raid on the Fortress of Köpenick' – the reference being of course to the classic German hoax of the 'captain of

Köpenick', where a shoemaker in 1906 procured a secondhand uniform of a Prussian captain, and took command of a squad of soldiers, arrested the local Bürgermeister, and confiscated the municipal treasury.

Clearly, *Window* was having a serious effect not only on the German defences but on Göring himself. On 8 October 1943 he called a meeting of his commanders and representatives of the industry and harangued them:

> In the field of radar they must have the world's greatest genius. They have the geniuses and we have the nincompoops ... The British would never have dared use the metal foil here if they had not worked out one hundred per cent what the antidote is. I hate the rogues like the plague, but in one respect I am obliged to doff my cap to them. After this war's over I'm going to buy myself a British radio set, as a token of my regard for their high frequency work. Then at last I'll have the luxury of owning something that has always worked.[1]

The running commentary delivered by the German ground controllers to their fighters was a prime target for British countermeasures. The British built a very powerful transmitter and called it *Aspidistra* (because it was the biggest in the world) and sent false orders to the German nightfighters telling them to land because of the threat of fog, and when the Germans found that the British were intervening in this way they immediately used women instead of men to transmit their instructions. But the British were ready for this and had German-speaking WAAFs standing by. The Germans then responded by having a man to repeat any orders the WAAF might give so that their nightfighters would realise that her orders were false. The British then got a man to repeat any orders that the German woman gave, and so it went on, until German exasperation reached the point where they played music to supplement their verbal orders. For example, jazz meant the bombers were in the Berlin area, waltzes indicated Munich, while the end of a raid was signified by *Alte Kamaraden*. This idea was promptly taken up by the British who retaliated in much the same way, the serious business of a war now drawing to its close being punctuated by moments of hilarity.

After the war Jones met Martini, Kammhuber and 'Beppo'

---

[1] Irving. *The Rise and Fall of the Luftwaffe*, p. 247

Schmid in their prisoner of war camp at Beaconsfield. Schmid was very forthright in his opinion that the British should have used *Window* at least six months before they did, and added that in his view the greatest mistake by the British was to use H_2S over Germany because 'it had been so treacherous in giving away the position of the bomber streams.' This opinion was also shared by Carl Bosch, a German scientist and an old friend of Jones from their earlier days at Oxford, who declared that he had heard H_2S transmissions from bombers over England while he was listening in Berlin. But as Jones points out, 'this opinion would have to be weighed against the damage to German industry that could not have been done without the aid of H_2S.'

Both Kammhuber and Martini were astonished at the 'completeness and accuracy' of the British information about German radar systems, Martini in particular wanting to know how it had been achieved. When Jones explained his own position Martini expressed even greater astonishment and pointed out that when the Germans were faced with a new British development they set up a committee to study the matter. Jones, who had had his own full share of committees, felt some sympathy: 'The Germans themselves may have had a Freudian abhorrence of committees because the standard word in German for "committee" is *Ausschuss* which, perhaps by more than coincidence, also means "rubbish".'

Many of the German systems taken as spoils of war were brought to Britain or examined *in situ*. The *Würzburg Riese* in particular became the mainstay of early work in radio-astronomy in the capable hands of Sir Martin Ryle, later Astronomer Royal, and a model of the *Riese* is still to be found in the RAF museum at Duxford. Other radars performed similar peaceful purposes in the hands of the Americans and French and other members of the Allies, and these, together with some radio-navigational beam systems, were still in employment many years after the war.

*

Of the pioneers of German radar, Christian Hülsmeyer received full recognition of his early work especially on the occasion of his 75th birthday in 1956. Among those paying tribute were the West German Chancellor Dr Konrad Adenauer on behalf of the state, General Martini, representing the Armed Forces of the new Germany, the Bürgermeisters of Munich and Düsseldorf, and representatives of the electronics industry including Professor Rukop of Telefunken, Professor Erhard, Professor Steinhoff, Professor Esau, Professor Leo Brandt and many more. A year later, on 31 January, Hülsmeyer died of a heart attack in a rest home in the Ahrweiler, and in 1981, a hundred years after his birth, a new barracks of a Rocket Regiment was erected near his birthplace of Eydelstedt and, during a ceremony attended by many dignitaries, was named the *Hülsmeyer Kaserne* in his honour.

Dr Rudolf Kühnhold held a responsible position in the new German Navy after the war until ill health forced him to retire. Now in his eighties (and convinced that he is the real inventor of radar) he lives a secluded life in his home town of Kiel where, so many years ago, he began his early experiments which led to the *Seetakt* and *Freya* systems. His son-in-law, Dr Claus Kinder, protects him from too much invasion of his privacy, but his defence system has been known to break down on occasions ...

His old antagonist Professor Wilhelm T. Runge rose to a very high position in the Telefunken complex and held it for many years, during which time he travelled the world lecturing on the development of Telefunken's systems. His fluent English, coupled with a droll humour, won him friends among a wide circle of the scientific field, and he maintained a lively interest in a range of technical subjects right up to his death at the age of 93 in June 1987 in his home town of Ulm.

General Martini also maintained his interest in radar techniques and signals communication and served on many radar committees after the war, and Kammhuber became the German Chief of Air Staff in the Supreme Headquarters of the Allied Powers in Europe (SHAPE) in 1956.

Dr Gotthard Müller, who performed such outstanding work for Lorenz, was a prisoner of the Russians for ten years before returning to his native Berlin and taking up a responsible position with SEL, as Lorenz is now known. From time to time he lectures in London and other capitals, as does that other indefatigable globe-trotter, Dr Herbert Kümmritz, who sallies forth from his native Ulm to give lectures in Britain and America.

Professor R.V. Jones still lives in Aberdeen, not very far from the University where, over the years, he has performed such outstanding work. Now Emeritus Professor in Natural Philosophy he is still active in scientific work and authorship, not to mention a great deal of lecturing and an occasional television appearance. Many of his contemporaries are, alas, no longer with us, but those who are, including Flight Sergeant Cox in his home town of Wisbech, still get together from time to time to recall those far-off days when in Churchill's words, they worked together under that 'white glow, overpowering, sublime, which ran through our island from end to end.'

And in quiet corners of Germany still live a dwindling number of scientists and engineers who contributed much to the German radar programme. They are not, as a rule, demonstrative men, preferring mainly to dwell among their thoughts and seek little acclaim for their achievements. But perhaps over a pipe or two in the evening, when the subject is raised, they will puff in silence for a minute or two then reach down a couple of glasses and a venerable bottle, and with the additional spirit of *Gemütlichkeit* the story is re-told.

Glossary of Technical Terms

'Acorn' valve: A small glass-enveloped valve with wire leads expressly designed for VHF and UHF working. An extrusion around its periphery gave it the appearance of an acorn in its cup.

Acquisition angle: The angle of an antenna pattern within which a target may be detected.

Amplitude modulation: Where the amplitude of a transmitter's carrier wave is varied by the superimposition of sound, i.e. speech, music, tones etc. The method is commonly used on the medium and long wave broadcast bands. (AM)

A/N bearings: A method of obtaining accurate bearings by switching the two halves of an antenna array in succession, thus 'sharpening' considerably its direction-finding characteristics.

Anode pulsing: Where the power to the anodes in a final stage of a transmitter is fed in successive bursts corresponding to the pulse rate frequency.

Antenna: The engineering term for an aerial.

Aspect of bearing: Most radar targets are of complex form, and their effective areas of reflection vary with both the wavelength used and the angle the radar beam 'sees' the target, in other words the *aspect*.

Bandpass filter: A device incorporated in a receiver (in this instance) which allows only a wanted band of frequencies to pass through it and attenuates adjacent channel signals.

Barkhausen-Kurz Principle: An early method of obtaining

centimetric oscillations. A suitable valve, normally a triode, was connected to its associated circuitry in an unorthodox way and its electrodes acted mainly as the tuned circuit. The output was very low, usually between 0.1 and 0.3 of a watt. See Fig. 4.

Base loading coil: A winding placed at the base of an antenna to enable the physical length of the antenna to be shortened while still maintaining the 'electrical length'.

Bremsröhre valve: A German valve used by them in the early days in the Barkhausen-Kurz oscillator. The name means a 'braking' or 'retarding field' valve and its purpose is explained more fully in Fig. 4.

Broadband antenna: RF (radio frequency) currents travel along the surface of a conductor. In the case of an antenna, particularly a transmitting antenna, too small a diameter restricts the useful bandwidth over which the transmitter can be tuned, while conversely, enlarging the diameter increases the bandwidth.

Cavity magnetron: Not to be confused with the earlier magnetrons used by Kühnhold, Runge, *et al.* The cavity magnetron was made from a solid block of copper with specially designed (and very secret) resonant cavities through which electrons were passed in such a way as to multiply their velocity an strength many times over.

Close resolution: The closeness with which a target will send back a distinguishable echo without swamping the radar receiver or causing other disturbances.

Co-axial cable: A cable having an insulated inner conductor entirely surrounded by another conductor in a cylindrically sheathed form and spaced at a certain maintained distance from each other in order to retain a specific *impedance* for radio purposes. The domestic TV aerial downlead is an example of this, though for transmitting purposes the diameter of the cable may be many times larger. It was designed at the turn of he century for use as submarine telegraph cable.

Coherer: An early form of detector – and there were many different versions – in which metallic or other conductive particles were enclosed in an insulated tube sealed with metal ends for connecting into a receiver circuit. On the reception of a signal the particles tended to bunch together or *cohere*, and they remained in this condition throughout the period of reception and afterwards, when the coherer had to be tapped to restore it to its normal state for future reception. Many ingenious devices were designed for this purpose.

Continuous waves: The unmodulated carrier of a transmitter. In the early days of wireless telegraphy the *carrier* (or continuous waves) of the transmitter was interrupted by a key in order to send morse, and even today radio telegraphists still refer to morse as 'CW' i.e. continuous waves.

CRT: Cathode-ray tube. In its most popular form the television picture tube. Early ones consumed vast quantities of electricity and were costly to run.

Deflection plates: The internal electrodes of a crt which, on being fed with high voltages, direct the electron stream from the cathode (the cathode-ray) to the fluorescent inner surface of the screen.

Deflection voltage: The voltage(s) applied to the above.

Dezimeter Telegraphie: The German code-name (Decimetre telegraphy) for their early radar.

Dipole: An antenna having two lengths of wire or rod and fed in the centre by a suitable feeder cable. The *half-wave dipole* is the commonest form.

Director: A length of wire or rod cut to a certain size and placed in front of a dipole at a spacing equivalent to a multiple of the operating wavelength. The currents set up in the director from the dipole, or *driven element*, direct the radio energy in the desired direction. Very often such an array incorporates a *reflector* (qv).

Doppler Effect: An effect discovered by the Austrian physicist Doppler in which the frequency of light, sound or other waves appears to increase when the source approaches an observer and to decrease when it passes. A popular example of this is the siren of a police car which rises in frequency as it approaches the listener and falls away when it passes. This is known as 'up Doppler' and 'down Doppler' respectively.

Echo declivity: The downward slope of an echo from the *effective echoing area* or *radar cross-section*. A function of the wavelength used and the shape of the target.

Echo trace: The trace or shape displayed on a crt as an indication of an echo, i.e. target.

EHT: Extra High Tension. The voltage applied to a crt, often many thousands of volts.

Enigma cipher: A mechanical encoding and decoding device invented and used by the Germans for enciphering their secret radio messages. It employed something similar to a typewriter keyboard, and when a key was depressed a number of wheels revolved in a predetermined order. Each wheel had a number of electrical contacts on its periphery and connected in such a way as to interchange the original keyed letters many times. It was successfully (and brilliantly) broken after much devoted time and trouble by the cryptographers at Bletchley Park.

FFO: The *Flugfunkforschungsinstitut*. The Airborne Radio Research Institute at Oberpfaffenhofen responsible for the research and design of many airborne equipments.

FMG: *Funkmessgeräte* or Radio measuring apparatus. The German term for radar in those days, sometimes known as *Funkmessortungsgeräte* (Radio Measuring Location Apparatus). Such designations often appeared as *FmG*, *FuMG* or *FuMO* according to the branch of the armed services employing the equipment.

Frequency modulation: A form of modulation in which the frequency of the transmitter carrier-wave is varied. Commonly called FM and now employed especially in the VHF broadcast bands and other channels.

Goniometer: Literally an instrument for measuring angles, in this instance the angles of a transmitted or received beam.

Harmonic: As in music, an 'overtone' of a fundamental frequency, i.e. in harmonic relationship to it. Thus in radio terms a harmonic of the fundamental frequency of, say, 1 MHz would be found at 2 MHz (the second harmonic) and at 3, 4 and 5 MHz (the third, fourth and fifth harmonic) and so on, according to the 'richness' of the oscillator in generating them.

Hertzian waves: The early name given to radio waves after Hertz their discoverer.

Hot cathode diode: A simple valve in which electrons are given off by a filament, or a cathode heated by a filament, and attracted to an anode which is positively charged. The modern semiconductor diode has long replaced it.

IF stage (s):   Intermediate frequency stage or stages. In a superheterodyne receiver the stages which amplify the *intermediate frequency* before the signal reaches the detector. Chiefly responsible for the selectivity of the receiver.

Ionosphere: Three main layers of ionisation at between 50 and 500 km above the earth's surface and known as the D, E and F layers, the F layer being 'split' into two separate layers called F1 and F2. These layers enable high frequency (short wave) radio signals to be 'bounced' around the world, and are often responsible for the changing conditions noticed on the short wave bands.

Lobes: The patterns of radio energy given off by an antenna. According to the type of antenna used there may be one main lobe and a number of smaller ones.

Low-frequency amplifier: Generally that part of a receiver following the detector stage which amplifies the audio, or *low-frequency*, component and delivers it to the loudspeaker. Similarly, public address systems are essentially low-frequency amplifiers.

Magnetron: An early form of cylindrical diode used for generating centimetric waves. Not to be confused with the cavity magnetron.

Maximum direction-finding: Where an antenna, particularly one designed for its directional qualities, receives a signal, either an echo or a transmitted signal, at maximum strengh. The principle is seen in modern receivers, especially portable or pocket receivers, where rotating the set in a particular direction results in a louder or clearer signal. The term is used here as distinct from *minimum direction-finding*, where the signal is received on the longitudinal axis of the antenna (as opposed to *maximum direction-finding* at 90° to the longitudinal axis) and is in fact a more precise method of determining the direction of a transmitting station. This latter method would be virtually useless for radar requirements since it depends for its precision on the *null point* (qv) of reception.

mW: Milliwatt, or one thousandth of a watt. The early experiments of Kühnhold and Runge were based upon valves which delivered about 0.1 watt of power, i.e. 100 mW.

Noise suppression: The function of a receiver to discriminate between the wanted signal and its own internal noise. It is generally measured in terms of the *decibel* (dB), and a good receiver will have a 'noise level', or noise suppression factor, of many dB's down.

Null point: That point of an antenna or other parts of a radio or electrical system where the energy is at a minimum.

Overall viewing screen: As implied, a screen which permits a quick overall view of the area covered by the radar before more accurate tuning for precise range, bearing or height. The provision of such a screen by the German authorities was considered useful in view of the relatively unskilled operators they had to employ.

Over-rating: Operating a valve (in this instance) at a higher voltage than that which it was designed for. With pulse techniques the valve was not running continuously, so over-rating was permissible within certain limits without damaging it.

Paraboloid: Or parabolic reflector. The bowl-shaped reflector now a common feature of most radar installations and also used extensively for microwave radio links and satellite television.

Pattern swinging: A method of changing the directional beam of a fixed antenna by electrical means, usually *phase conversion*.

Phase conversion: The changing or conversion of alternating currents, in this case RF (radio frequency) currents, so that while their frequency and amplitude are equal a time lag or *phase difference* exists between them. Thus they are not performing the similar parts of their cycles at the same instant.

Polarisation: In this case, vertical or horizontal polarisation. A transmitting antenna erected in the vertical plane is said to be *vertically polarised*, and its signal is best received on a vertical receiving antenna, particularly where VHF and UHF transmission is concerned. Over a long distance, and to some extent depending on the frequency used, this is not so important since temperature inversions and other propagation features tend to bend the path of the signal. A compromise is often made with a *cross-polarised* antenna.

Power amplifier: The final stage of a transmitter which amplifies the radio energy and delivers it to the antenna by means of various forms of coupling.

PPI: Plan Position Indicator. (See text)

Pre-set frequency:In this instance a receiver whose reception of signals on certain frequencies has been pre-determined and which are selected by a switch as opposed to manual tuning. Some domestic receivers, particularly in the thirties, employed this principle.

PRF: Pulse Rate Frequency. The number of times in one second that a number of pulses are generated and transmitted.

PRU: Photographic Reconnaissance Unit.

Push-pull: A system in which a pair of valves or solid state devices are so connected that, in the case of a valve, the grid of one is negative while the other is positive and, as a result the anode current of one valve is rising as the other is falling. The method can be used in a number of applications, but particularly for the audio output stages of receivers and amplifiers, or the RF stages of receivers and transmitters.

Radio altimeter: An altimeter using the time taken for a radio signal to reach the earth from an aircraft and to return, in such a way as to indicate the height.

Radio lens: A method of focusing a radio beam in a special antenna by means of lenses made from certain materials, sometimes non-conductive. The principle is similar to that of optical lenses and was first researched by Hertz.

Radome: Contraction of 'radar dome'. An insulated cover or 'blister' on an aircraft, containing the radar antenna(s) and often the means of rotation.

Receiver muting: A method of switching off a receiver electronically during transmission pulses to prevent overloading. A similar principle is often employed in communications receivers where a bias voltage is applied to render certain stages inoperative during transmission periods.

Reflector: An element placed at a certain distance behind a radiating dipole to increase the forward direction of the transmitted energy.

RPM: Revolutions per minute.

Sinusoidal waveform: The form or shape of a *sine-wave*, that is, the characteristic shape of an alternating current, in this case a radio frequency current, where the nodes and antinodes of its amplitude are shown against time as a series of cycles or curves.

S-meter: A meter inserted into the circuitry of a receiver to give an indication of signal strength.

Solenoid: A form of electro-magnet with a core which, upon excitation by a current, can be made to move and perform a number of functions. The principle of the two-tone door chimes is often based on this.

Stray fields: Electromagnetic waves which have 'escaped' from their source, usually through lack of suitable screening, or which have been unintentionally generated. They can be an extreme nuisance.

Superhet: The *superheterodyne* receiver, in which the incoming signal is mixed with the frequency of a local oscillator and the product, sum or difference of the latter becomes the *intermediate frequency* (See IF stage (s)). The idea is to eliminate the need for a large number of manually tuned stages by this conversion to a fixed frequency.

Super-regenerative receiver: A type of receiver where the incoming signal is greatly amplified by pushing the detector stage to the threshold of oscillation, often in conjunction with a 'quench' oscillation on a supersonic level.

Thyratron: From the Greek, meaning 'door'. A form of gas-filled triode where the grid is usually a cylinder surrounding the cathode and containing an annular disc. An aperture in this disc faces a cup-shaped anode, and the function of the grid is to control the flow of electrons to the anode in the sense of an on-off switch. Such a device is said to 'strike' instead of 'conduct'.

TRE: Telecommunications Research Establishment.

TRF receiver: *Tuned Radio Frequency* receiver. A receiver which amplifies and detects the signal on its incoming frequency, as opposed to the superhet where the frequency is changed. These sets were popular before the war and depended for their selectivity and sensitivity on the adjustment of a 'reaction' control which was meant to push the detector to the point where oscillation nearly but not quite took place. Very often this was overdone by unskilled or careless persons, and the detector was driven to the point where the set behaved like a small transmitter, causing severe interference to nearby listeners.

Triode: A valve with three electrodes: cathode, grid and anode.

Waveguide: A form of hollow tube in which radio energy is 'guided' or driven, especially for frequencies of 3,000 MHz and above. The effective power is thus considerably enhanced.

Yagi antenna: A form of directional antenna designed by Professor Hidetsugu Yagi of Japan in the 1920's. It usually consists of a dipole driven element, a reflector, and a number of director elements, all of which serve to increase the effective forward power of the transmitted beam. Such an antenna is also used for reception, the usual form of domestic television aerial is an example of a Yagi antenna.

Index of Radar and Auxiliary Systems

General Index